JOH

HAVING
A BINGE
ON A
DIET

JOHN TOVEY'S

HAVING A BINGE ON A DIET

NETWORK BOOKS

Network Books is an imprint of BBC Books,
a division of BBC Enterprises Limited,
Woodlands, 80 Wood Lane,
London W12 0TT

First published 1993
Text © John Tovey 1993
Cartoons © Gray Jolliffe 1993
Edited by Susan Fleming
ISBN 0 563 36471 8
Set in 11/14½ Palatino
Printed and bound in Great Britain by Clays Ltd, St Ives Plc
Cover printed by Clays Ltd, St Ives Plc

CONTENTS

INTRODUCTION

Before sitting down at the word processor to start this book, I decided to seek out my old photograph albums which I hadn't seen for more years than I cared to remember. I couldn't for the life of me think where they were, and spent several days looking in the obvious places, both at the house in Bowness and down at the farm. Suddenly it clicked, and I went to the drawer in the Bowness lounge to find it just wouldn't budge an inch. I had to call the joiner who, rather than damage the American yew fitted unit, took the top shelves and cupboard down and then unscrewed the base of these and the lid of the drawer unit. And there they all were – warm, and a little faded around the edges, as they had been sitting close to a large radiator for at least fourteen years!

Initially I was delighted to see them, but as I started turning over the pages and looking at the black and white photographs I suddenly realised I had *always* been overweight – in fact in some shots, quite obese and gross. As a naked baby, frolicking on the lambswool rug in a photograph taken profession-ally in one of the studios so popular in those days, I had triple chins, wobbly thighs and the largest bum possible. Angelically dressed as a chorister in my cassock, surplice and white collar in a shot from the local evening paper, I looked as if I was six months gone and hadn't told my mother! The surplice just showed up the surplus fat, and there was no need for a choir stall to hold the music of 'Where sheep may safely graze' as I could use my paunch! I looked as if I were forever grazing.

There were some photos, too, from my days at the grammar school. A picture of me in drag dressed as one of the sisters in *The Admirable Crichton* looked as if I hadn't needed padding anywhere, but that I could be easily kneaded. The shots on the Union Castle ship *Windsor Castle*, when I sailed out to Cape Town in 1950, all show me holding something to eat or posing *with* food. And the photos of my early days in Central Africa are very funny indeed. One close to a waterfall and bathing pool make me look more like a Buddha from Bombay than a boy from Barrow-in-Furness. And so they go on . . .

But it wasn't until I saw one taken in New York in March 1990 that I felt quite disgusted with myself. At the end of February that year, I had returned from my annual eight-week break in the sunny Cape where, although I walked on the mountain each morning, I knew so many people involved with food and wine that I spent the rest of each day sampling the grape and dabbling with the beautiful local produce. Not content with that, after three days back at the hotel catching up on the mail and sorting out opening for the season, six of us flew to New York to present our annual stint of a week of cooking dinner for up to

8

seventy guests each evening on the theme of 'English Country House Cooking' at the Union League Club.

My editor on *Lloyd's Log*, on hearing I was to be in New York for a week, asked if he could have an update on the restaurant scene as part of my series of articles on travel and food. No problem at all, as when I start on a binge, it is a relatively simple task to continue. . . So it was two light up-market 'testing' luncheons each day, then cooking dinner at night. (I need to add that I am a *taster* and tester cook. I'm not content with the end bit of each leg of lamb I am carving, but it has to be dipped in the rich cream onion nutmeg sauce, and the roast fanned potatoes cooked in duck fat have to be tasted and tested as well.) The evenings were rounded off by me taking the team out to relatively inexpensive bistros – this would make for a better balanced article.

The article may have been well balanced, but towards the end of the week I was finding myself ruddy uncomfortable as my knickers were tight, the buttons on my shirts were all about to pop, and there were oval pieces of sun-tanned flesh apparent to all and sundry between them. Changing into my travelling tracksuit on the flight back from New York was a gymnastic feat I could barely accomplish – you know how small airline toilets are! I had to stand on the seat of the loo to remove my tight slacks and bursting knickers, ease myself into the lightweight trousers and then struggle with the upper garments. As I waddled back to my lounger-seat in first class, I felt like the original Michelin Man, and knew people were staring at me.

It was only when I got back to the house in Bowness, had thrown my dirty laundry and clothes into the spare bedroom and was getting out of the bath that I took a look at myself in the mirror. I was horrified. In a loud voice I simply said, 'Tovey, you are disgusting.' The friendly voice of my house-keeper from the open-plan lounge said, 'Oh, Mr T., think positively', which I immediately did. Taking a further look at myself, I said in an even louder voice, 'Tovey, you are *positively* disgusting!'

In the post when I returned was the *BBC Diet* book by Dr Barry Lynch, as well as a letter from the eminent man himself giving me the scheduled dates for the rehearsals and recording of the series which was broadcast in Autumn 1991, called *John Tovey's Entertaining on a Plate*. The thought of appearing on camera like a bloated baboon did not appeal to me and so I decided to do something about it. I was fifteen and a half stone, and I needed to lose about two and a half of those.

My first thought was that I'd done this on so many occasions before that my friends and staff could hardly take me seriously any more. Name any diet and I bet you I've been on it. The only one that ever appealed to me was the fun Sea Food diet – when you saw food you ate it! I had wagging fingers and naughty seaside picture postcards stuck to the doors of the fridges, I went on carbohydrate diets, protein pledges, fruit fasts, egg, grapefruit and cottage cheese in every possible shape and form, and visited health farms annually where I frequently shed up to eleven pounds in ten to fourteen days, but put it back and more in the same period of time when I got out.

But determined now to shed a couple of stone, I made up my mind to go on Barry's *BBC Diet*. I stuck to it resolutely for the first four days but on the fifth, when I was supposed to have a steamed fillet of plaice, my body, palate and belly craved a grilled fatty lamb chop. And a grilled fatty lamb chop I had. Bang goes yet another diet, I thought – but it didn't, quite. Working alongside Barry while planning the filming in Cardiff, I talked and talked and talked about food, and learned a great deal.

I realised – rightly or wrongly – that there just wasn't a diet written that could possibly suit every single person, and where I had always gone wrong in the past was in my constantly becoming bored, frustrated and depressed due to the lack of goodies which I adore so much. I then discovered and developed a way of gently shedding the surplus fat at the rate of one and a half pounds each and every week without interfering with my hectic lifestyle – and this is literally centred around the very two things that were awful for me, food and drink. Without holding anything back I will tell you straight here and now, I never had to cut down on my drinking (see p. 54). In fact, when one is endeavouring to shed the surplus pounds, drink can be a lovely comforter.

At the beginning of the diet it was time for my annual private health check, but my friendly doctor did say that as I was over fifty I was entitled to a check-up each three years on the National Health. Never one to let a bargain go by, I made an appointment at the local health centre, on whose books I had been for close on twenty-five years. I duly arrived at the appointed hour and was questioned by a relatively new nursing assistant in charge of preventive medicine. Name: 'John Tovey.' Address: 'Miller Howe.' Date of birth: '19 May 1933.' Occupation: 'Director.' Director of what? 'Well, certainly not the traffic.' Frozen, frosty stare. Do you smoke? 'No.' Do you drink? 'Yes.' How much? 'A bottle and a half a day.' Good God, you don't! 'Yes, I do, and at this rate I'll be needing a drink any minute so forget about the medical, I'll go back to private medicine.'

A bottle and a half of wine is consumed by me daily with joy and relish and it got me through the weight problem. I travelled and dined out as before, and I never once felt deprived. Perhaps, on reflection, it was a trifle tricky to begin with, but I can honestly say that having shed three stone (and more important still, having kept it off), I am a very much happier person. Actually going into a menswear shop and selecting a pair of trousers or jacket without mocking looks and shrieks of 'Nothing your size, sir', have made the effort worthwhile. And, when somebody in a bar or restaurant smiles at *me*, and not at the person beside me, it is worth a million.

I went for another medical after sixteen months on my diet. As I was connected to the new-fangled, computerised scale, the nurse enquired about the weight loss. I proudly and loudly proclaimed I was down to twelve stone. After checking on the machine, she turned to me and said in a very down-to-earth Lancashire voice, 'Thou's not, you know, you're twelve stone seven and that's for sure.' My blood pressure must have rocketed up, and I couldn't get it out of my mind until I got back to the farm. Her scale might have said twelve stone seven; mine stated twelve stone. Next day I had my housekeeper stand on it and it showed her to be seven pounds less than she knew her weight was. I must have been *sixteen* stone all those months ago!

However, all's well that ends well. The medical revealed that my cholesterol level was terrific, my blood pressure had never been so good, my stress level was strong, and when I went on the coronary pace-walk machine I felt I could have continued for thirty minutes instead of giving up after eleven as I did the year before! The diet, quirky as it might be, had really worked, helping me lose weight and to become fitter.

Folk I haven't seen for some time are always slightly shell-shocked when they see me, and I find myself answering endless questions. I occasionally hesitate, as I don't in any way wish to sound like a born-again Christian. But I *am* a born-again person, as I can actually see the outline of my bone structure once more. I hope it will work as well for you.

John Tovey

CHAPTER 1

BINGE
DIET
'RULES'

Having talked to Barry Lynch in great detail after failing to continue with the excellent diet in his *BBC Diet*, I sat down and took a hard, serious look at the facts. I realised that in the past, when I had taken it into my head to do something about my bulges, I went out and purchased the latest diet craze book, never read it thoroughly from cover to cover, and soon became disenchanted as the diet didn't work.

I would religiously keep to it for the first day, feeling slightly virtuous and not all that deprived of food. The second day would have me constantly looking at my watch thinking, surely it is elevenses or lunchtime? I would be starting to feel the strain mentally, and not sleeping very well because of constant dreams (near nightmares often) about food. The third day was when I usually developed complete withdrawal symptoms and found myself unable to read a magazine or look at television as, more often than not, the first page I flicked over, or channel I tuned to, would be displaying the most luscious, lavish advert for some delicious item of food. It would be then – bad-tempered, hungry and dispirited – that I would weigh myself, but to little avail. I wanted to see the pounds come off and the inches disappear within those three short days. And it just doesn't work as fast as that.

Unreasonable and silly, you might say, but I used to be both when it came to dieting. Seldom did I get through one week and even if I did, when I got on the scales again (having, I must admit, cheated perhaps two or three times with half a Mars Bar or a small chunk of Lancashire cheese), I simply said 'Not worth the ruddy effort' and went back to the comforts of *real food*. And not just the usual amounts, but *double*, as I would be so depressed and annoyed with myself for having failed once again in my efforts.

The Fun Element

The trouble with me, of course, is that I'm an unrepentant foodie, and I live and work continually surrounded by food. I'm rather 'spoiled' in that I have experienced so much deliciousness throughout my eating life, and have come indeed to take it for granted. Any diet which spells out what I've to eat and what to avoid on a daily basis – and, worst of all, *when* – is therefore bound to be, for me, the most utter tedium. It's probably this way for many others as well: as we've all become much more sophisticated about food, the blandness and monotony of the generality of slimming diets make them become all the more unappetising and unworkable.

It's not that the diets are bad in themselves, it's just that they are boring. Neither is any one diet going to work for everyone, even though it may be sound and sensible. We all have psychological preferences which make some diets more appealing than others. For many people, counting calories religiously is the thing; for others, grouping foods into those allowed or forbidden has worked; and some martyrs have managed to lose weight on single-ingredient diets (grapefruit or pineapple only, for instance) or those dreary packet supplements. None of these is necessarily better or worse than another: it's just that there will be one that has to appeal to you before it can possibly work for you.

Well, I've done all that, I've been there, and nothing *had* worked, probably for the following reason. In every single one of my books, and my radio and television broadcasts, I've always emphasised my *love* of food. It really is my favourite subject, and eating it is my favourite hobby, and gives me my greatest pleasure in life (apart from wine, but that's another part of the story). Food is fun, was and is my constant theme. Any mealtime is meant to be enjoyable anyway, an unchanging part of our collective social sense and our individual psychology. When this pleasure element is missing (as in most diets), conflicts are quickly set up in the dieter, and the stresses of hunger, boredom and the loss of that pleasure set the stage for a quick return to non-dietary guzzling.

So, any diet that was going to work for me had to be fun, and had to incorporate elements that would help avoid any hunger, boredom and those feelings

19

of guilt if or when I slipped from my pedestal. It didn't take me long to work out the 'rules', once I'd considered all the options from the diets I'd digested over the years, and indeed there are elements of many different dietary philosophies here – just reinterpreted in the inimitable Tovey way!

Firstly, there *are* no hard and fast rules – which is probably why it's been so successful for me. By accepting that I'm only human, that I can be tempted occasionally, I have a far more relaxed attitude to everything, and eating – even if to a dietary plan – can still be fun. I think anyway that life would be depressingly dull if we had to stick to the same rules seven days a week, four weeks a month, and twelve months a year. In a way, rules are often made to be broken . . .

Common sense and that sense of fun are the key elements in my eating plan, so you don't require a degree in either mathematics or nutritional science in order to be able to understand or follow it. In short, the rules are:

1. Avoid fattening foods.

2. Seek out healthier foods.

3. Eat less in general.

4. Cook in a healthier way.

5. Concentrate on flavour.

6. Allow the occasional binge.

7. Take some exercise.

Two or so years after starting on this diet I feel like a new man, for not only have I lost near to three stone in weight – the first time in my life that dieting has been successful – but never on one single occasion have I felt either depressed or deprived. I actually feel fitter, am mentally brighter, and have won back my self-respect (well on the way out, so disgusted was I with my figure). I'm also extraordinarily *proud* of myself, and I hope the ideas, advice and confessions in the following pages will help *you* to feel the same about yourself.

Tovey Before and After

The first thing I did was to actually sit and write down on paper what my eating pattern had generally been over the last year or so. Then, and only then, did I realise what a little pig I had become.

THEN . . .

My day always starts with my Old English sheepdog Ozzie jumping on to the bed at exactly ten to seven (it only takes her one or two days to adjust to the putting back and forward of the clocks twice a year, believe it or not). I used, then, to get up, let her out, make myself a pot of tea and take it and a few home-made biscuits back to bed to watch breakfast TV for half an hour.

As soon as I got in to work at the hotel, it was a large glass of fresh orange juice for me, and corn-flakes and milk for the dog. The minute breakfast service was over at around ten I was into the kitchen like a streak of lightning, and any kidneys left over were for me (woe betide the breakfast chef if he hadn't cooked enough!). These were helped along with a couple of rashers of well-done fatty bacon and a large Cumberland sausage, all chopped up and put inside two warm, freshly baked morning baps (which were very liberally buttered, I might add).

At elevenses (only one hour later) it was time for

coffee and just a bit of shortbread from the bake-house. Lunch, at home, would be baked beans with poached egg on toast or some bobotie with pasta, and always a sweet left over from the hotel dinner the night before. The walk with Ozzie would never be more than thirty minutes – sufficient time to allow her to attend to the simple calls of nature and have a good sniff! Egyptian PT (a snooze, for the uninitia-ted) was then the order of the afternoon and around four it was teatime, with scones and a wedge of cream sponge or slice of rich fruit cake.

The evenings were murder as it was a matter of tasting this and trying that when preparing dinner in the kitchen. Not in teaspoon or miniature portions, I hasten to add, but ruddy big dollops. When carving the nightly roast the first slice of each leg was for *me* – the one with all the beautiful fat and skin on it. During the slight pause between dishing up dinners in batches of twelve plates, I would always find the fatty, well cooked end bits which are so sweet and succulent, but *so* sinful. Having done my nightly walk round the tables in the dining room, it would be time for the kitchen brigade and I to have our meal. I kidded myself I was only having the main course (very occasionally a pud too), but obviously ignored all the mouthfuls which had been shovelled away during the two or so hours' run-up to the service of dinner.

Getting home at around ten-thirty at night would

be the time for winding down, possibly eating a second pudding taken from the hotel, or having a few chocolate nuts. I would then end the day with a very large beaker of hot chocolate made from full-fat milk, with lots of dark chocolate and nutmeg grated on top of the frothy mix.

No wonder I was obese. On reflection, I think I must also have been slightly insane!

. . . AND NOW

Now my normal eating pattern is as follows, but please don't think you will achieve this the first week, as you won't. In fact, you mustn't. Slowly, slowly does it.

When Ozzie wakes me in the morning now, it is half a lemon squeezed into a small glass of warm water and I sip this slowly whilst watching breakfast TV. When I arrive at the hotel it is a glass of freshly squeezed orange juice and then two thin slices of our home-made muesli bread with one tomato thinly sliced on to a baking tray, liberally sprinkled with freshly ground black pepper, baked, then transferred to the bread to make a sloppy but satisfying sandwich. I eat nothing with my coffee at elevenses, or at lunchtime, but when taking Ozzie on her hour and a half daily walk (come wind, rain or high water!), I invariably eat a couple of apples or an apple and a very large peeled carrot. At teatime it is a light brew of a poncy tea which I have taken to – mango, blackcurrant or peach – with neither milk nor sugar. Again, nothing to eat.

When I get back to the hotel to sign the post at around five-thirty, I have a large cup of hot Bovril, and I now only work in the kitchen during the serving of the meal. Woe betide me if I find myself picking – I get hell from the kitchen staff. We then sit down to our supper of the main course, but I pick out my selection of veg or have a small salad made up to go with the meat. No fat or chicken skin is ever put on my plate, and I eat the smaller portion much more slowly.

This is all I allow myself (plus, I must admit, a modicum of wine, see p. 54), but I must emphasise again that I have worked my way slowly and carefully to this. You cannot just plunge into such an eating pattern and expect your body to be happy about it. Absorb the *ideas* and 'rules' first, then adjust, adopt and adapt them to your own life.

> Never sit down to what looks like an empty plate: fill up the spaces where you might have had roast potatoes or chips with masses of green veg.

Rule No. 1

Avoid Fattening Foods

As I'm sure you all know, recent nutritional guide-lines have advised us to cut down on our intake of fat and sugar. These are actually guidelines for health, but also have enormous relevance for the dieter.

FAT

This is the most damaging of all the food that you ingest, and you will have to avoid it as much as possible. You might think at this moment that this will be no problem whatsoever, but I don't know a soul who, initially, didn't find it terribly difficult to avoid fatty foods at times.

There are two types of fat, saturated and unsatura-ted, and the difference between them lies in their chemical make-up of fatty acids. Most foods contain a mixture of both types. **Saturated fats** are mostly found in dairy products and meats, in coconut and palm oils, hard margarines and cooking fats. The particular combination of fatty acids in these con-tributes to the build-up of cholesterol in the blood,

> Skim off the fat from the top of casseroles, stews and gravies.

27

which can increase the risk of heart disease, and they should be avoided. **Unsaturated fats**, mainly the oils, are further divided into monounsaturated and polyunsaturated, and these names again refer to different combinations of fatty acids.

Monounsaturated oils, which include olive and peanut, are considered fairly neutral in a health and dietary sense, neither bad for you (as are saturated) nor directly beneficial. (Olive oil, for instance, consists of 10 per cent saturated fat, 75 per cent monounsaturated and 10 per cent polyunsaturated.) Most experts now think polyunsaturated oils are the healthiest, containing least saturates and the most polyunsaturates. The best is safflower (10 per cent saturated, 75 per cent polyunsaturated), followed by sunflower, soya and corn.

We all need a small amount of fat in our diets to provide energy, certain vitamins and to make the food tasty. The two fatty acids which we need and that our bodies cannot synthesise are both polyunsaturated, which actually suggests that there really is no *nutritional* need to eat any saturated fats. But we do, and too much of them, which is both unhealthy *and* fattening.

The leanest cuts of beef are rump and fillet steak (also, of course, the most expensive!).

28

MEATS All red meats contain saturated fats and, although you can cut the visible stuff off steaks or chops, there is an invisible marbling of fat through the flesh which is virtually impossible to avoid. This, ironically, is what makes meat *taste* good. Always buy the leanest possible cuts, and when buying mince, look for the word 'lean' on the packet. Better still, buy your own lean meat, remove any visible fat, then mince it at home.

Farmed venison is the meat with the lowest flesh fat levels. Rabbit is good as well.

Avoid all pâtés, salamis and sausages, as saturated fat is a major constituent. While experimenting with recipes for this book, we baked a sausage in a small baking tray for 30 minutes; we were *amazed* at the amount of fat coming out of such a small piece of food! An individual pork pie, for instance, has 1¼ oz (30 g) of fat! And bacon, too, is out, which I find a disaster: one serving has about 1 oz (25 g) of fat.

White meats like chicken or turkey are not marbled in the same way as red meat, but poultry skins contain fat. I found this the most difficult thing to stop eating, as the skin of a traditional Sunday roast chicken is so full of flavour. But in testing this, we removed the skin from a chicken breast, weighed it in at 1 oz (25 g), then baked it. The fat that was rendered was virtually the same weight!

Avoid duck, which is very fatty, but game birds are good to eat, and low in fat.

BUTTER Another visible saturated fat is butter, and I miss this the most. I used to admonish those bungling bureaucrats in Brussels for amassing such mountains of the stuff when it should have been sold at a lower price to us tax-paying citizens. Now I hardly ever use it for myself and, apart from in pastries and cakes, I seldom serve it to visitors at home. Margarine is no better as, like butter, by law it must contain at least 82 per cent fat (the rest is water); although it may be labelled 'high in polyunsaturates', it has the same amount of calories. Anything with less fat must be called a spread, and although these can be used for spreading and cooking, I find them pretty revolting, and would rather do without. Sandwiches and toast don't truly *need* butter anyway (see p. 98), and there are several alternatives to its use in cooking.

OILS Oils actually contain more fat than butter (100 per cent as opposed to 82 per cent), but as most are unsaturated, they are not too damaging so long as the intake is modest. Once upon a time I used them lavishly, particularly extra virgin olive oil and the rich pungent walnut oil. I turned my nose up at poor little sunflower oil, but I now use it quite a lot of the time. Although olive oil, being monounsaturated, is considered less healthy, I continue to use it in cooking because of its wonderful flavour. And there has also been a lot of discussion lately about the benefits of the 'Mediterranean diet', which inevitably includes a lot of olive oil.

I couldn't do without oil in my cooking, particularly since I don't now use butter, but use just a smidgen (even of walnut, as the merest whiff can go such a long way). As I've said, most foods are a mixture of both types of fat: this is why you must look for oils that are labelled low in saturates, high in polyunsaturates.

EGGS Egg yolks are high in cholesterol, so I tend to avoid them these days. The recommended allowance is only three to five per week anyway, or one to three for those at risk of cholesterol damage to blood vessels (smokers, those with heart problems etc).

CREAM, CHEESE AND MILK Cream used to be one of the foundation stones of much of my cooking. It still features in many dishes at the hotel, but I never touch it myself now. Cheese is a rare treat too, as I'm not really very interested in cottage cheese (4 per cent fat) and everything else has high percentages (although a low-fat Cheddar is now available, at 14 per cent rather than about 30).

I thought I could never do without the rich local milk, as I was used to having it on cereal, in tea, to drink before I went out for an evening's merrymaking (to line my stomach), and in my bedtime drink. I cut down gradually, trying low-fat powdered stuff at first; in an attempt to make it more palatable I added an extra tablespoon to the mix, but I gradually reverted to faithfully following the instructions on the packet. (I must confess, though, that powdered milk is one thing Ozzie just will not tolerate. Her daily cornflakes have to have the real thing on them or else she just takes a sniff, gives me the cold shoulder, and retreats under the kitchen table at the farm to sulk.)

I've now been able to reduce my desires and use skimmed milk for drinking and cooking. This has virtually no fat at all, although containing the same protein and calcium as full-fat milk. Coffee I always drink black anyway, but coming from the North of England, I was a constant brewer up and imbiber of tea which, during the course of a normal day, would see a hellish amount of cow juice devoured. I now drink weak fruit and herb teas which are delightfully flavoured and don't need any milk added.

(I must admit that my latest post-diet medical showed a decrease in calcium levels in my body. This, I must assume, is the result of my cutting out almost all dairy products. Since then, when Ozzie

We develop a taste for sweet and salty foods in childhood, so look after the next generation by *not* adding any extra salt or sugar to your children's food.

has her weekly milk, egg and honey – so good for her coat, and how she slurps it down – I drink a half pint of milk myself, and I savour every sip.)

OTHER FOODS There are hidden fats in bought and manufactured goods like crisps (one packet contains about ⅓ oz or 9 g), chocolate, biscuits, cakes and ice-cream. Nuts and oily fish, such as sardines, herring, mackerel, trout and pilchards, contain poly-unsaturated fats.

SUGAR

Of all the things we eat, only sucrose – cane or beet sugar – provides calories without providing anything else in the way of nourishment. It actually is damaging too, encouraging bacteria in the mouth and contributing directly to tooth decay. If thinking in terms of calories, 10 teaspoons or 1 oz (25 g) of sugar contains 110, the same as a grilled lamb cutlet (which also has proteins, vitamins and bulk). I know which I'd rather have to fill me up!

Luckily I've never sweetened tea or coffee, but I do use a certain amount of sugar in baking (this I've managed to cut down). To satisfy my occasional desire for sweet things, I have taken to eating a lot of fresh fruit; this contains fructose, which is the sweetest of all the different types of sugar. (I'm sure it's also contributed to a noticeable improvement in my skin texture.)

But there are hidden and disguised sugars in so many things, particularly processed foods. The fruit in bought jams, for instance, is nearly matched weight for weight in sugar content; I now use diabetic jams, which have reduced sugar, or simply spread a puréed fruit on toast. Bought cereals have high proportions of both sugar and salt (see p. 70). A small carton of fruit yoghurt – which we all think so healthy – contains *1 tablespoon* of sugar, and all the bought drinks – lemonade, cola, tonic water, health drinks and children's squashes – contain quite unacceptable levels. I don't even need to mention sweets and chocolate, but I'm afraid I'll never to be able to look a Mars Bar in the face again (one bar contains *nine* teaspoons of sugar).

Rule No. 2

Seek Out Healthier Foods

Perhaps the first piece of advice should be that when shopping, do look at the new labels on products. Although I still find them a bit confusing to decipher, they do list, *in order of quantity*, all that is in the product. So if sugar comes before fruit in the ingredients in a jam, think twice about it! This gives you an invaluable insight into what you are potentially going to put into your body.

VEGETABLES AND FRUIT

The healthiest foods of all are those that are fresh, not processed, and as far as your diet is concerned, that means fruit and vegetables.

Vegetables to me are fun food, and as well as serving a selection of seven to accompany the main course at a Miller Howe dinner, I've also written a whole book about them. Many of those recipes would not be relevant in our diet – they use lots of butter and oil, for instance – but the raw ingredients

An apple eaten raw with its skin gives you fibre and Vitamin C. The latter is lost in cooking.

are still there in all their colourful and flavourful variety, to be served raw or cooked in as great a variety of ways. I could never be a vegetarian, but a few non-meat meals per week, or meals in which the vegetable quantity is considerably greater than that of meat can help your health as well as your figure (a salad with a smidgen of meat, perhaps, or a pasta or rice dish).

Even vegetables which we think of as fattening, such as potatoes, are healthy, and they're never off my food list. They are 80 per cent water, and contain good amounts of Vitamin C and potassium; these nutrients are near the skin of the potato, so cook in the skins rather than peel first. Dieters may actually devour them in reasonable quantity, just not smothered with masses of butter (see p. 103 for some ideas). A baked potato has 25 calories per 1 oz (25 g) weight, new boiled potatoes 20. (Chips have 70 calories per 1 oz (25 g); and thin ones have over double the amount of fat of thick chips. Avoid them at all costs.)

Fruit is best eaten raw, as a snack, and to satisfy that craving for sweetness.

Bean sprouts are very nutritious, with three to five times more Vitamin C than the beans from which they grew.

FISH

We should all eat very much more fish, and I've taken to grilling prime pieces, or baking them whole. Most fish have a very low fat content, and even what we call oily fish are more valuable than detrimental. Vitamin D is only found in oily fish and a few other foods, and oily fish, such as salmon and mackerel, also supply essential fatty acids which can protect from heart disease.

FIBRE

Raw vegetables and fruit are better for you than cooked in a nutritional sense, with their full complement of vitamins and minerals, and because of the chewing and bulk, can make your stomach feel you're getting *more* in the way of food. This is because most fruit and vegetables contain good quantities of fibre, the cellulose which forms the main structure of food plants. Because it is indigestible, it can keep you feeling fuller for longer. Even just chewing fibre foods is good and helps the dieter, because chewing gives a psychological satisfaction.

Fish canned in oil is much higher in calories than fresh fish.

Other fibre foods are cereals, pulses or dried beans (the famous baked beans without sugar are good), wholemeal flour, bread, pasta and rice. For instance, I adore pasta, and have it a lot, served with a heavily reduced fresh tomato sauce or pesto sauce (see pp. 96 and 162), and yes, occasionally, the merest pinch of freshly grated Parmesan. People think pasta is fattening, but you need a *certain* amount of starch and fibre to keep you going.

Increasing the fibre in the diet – by about 50 per cent, or about 1¼ oz (30 g) daily – is another health and diet recommendation. It's easy enough to include a fibre food at every meal.

Store green vegetables in a cool dark place to preserve their colour and thus their nutrients.

DAIRY REPLACEMENTS

To replace the full-fat creams and cheeses that add such texture and flavour to so many dishes, I have now taken to using the lower-fat *crème fraîche*, natural yoghurts, and *fromage frais* or *blanc*. Never forget to look at the labels to verify fat content.

Crème fraîche is a cream treated with a culture which gives it a slightly sour, acid taste, which I find appealing. Its fat content is a third that of double cream. Mixed with a little runny honey, it looks very like whipped cream, and will satisfy you – and your guests – if used to accompany a bowl of fruit etc. It can also be gently heated, and does not curdle.

Low-fat natural yoghurts can hold as little as 0.1 per cent fat, but being mucked around so much, they may contain non-milk thickeners or stabilisers. Most natural yoghurts will have about 3 per cent fat; ewe's milk Greek yoghurt about 6 per cent fat; and cow's milk Greek yoghurt about 10 per cent fat. Many yoghurts need a little cornflour to stabilise them when heated, in a sauce, say.

Fromage frais or *blanc* is a fresh cheese made from skimmed milk with no fat solids. I adore it. It was

---

Remember you don't have to finish everything on your plate.

---

once traditionally made in Luxembourg, but is now mass-produced all over Europe, particularly in France where it is eaten rather like yoghurt, as a pudding and to accompany fresh fruit. It can have between 1 and 8 per cent fat content. Do read the labels carefully.

If you were a nibbler – of crisps, biscuits or chocolate – change to apples, celery, carrots and seedless grapes (at least they're the *shape* of the Maltesers I used to adore!).

Rule No. 3

Eat Less in General

Having sat down and thought seriously about my eating habits (and you must do the same before you embark on your new way of life), I soon realised that I ate far too much, quite apart from my gluttonous consumption of things like butter and cream. (Look back to the beginning of this chapter, if you doubt my words.) It was a struggle at first not to dollop whipped double cream on to puds, lavishly spread butter on to my thick hot toast, or soak a salad in an oil-rich dressing. I now can sympathise with reformed addicts, whether of alcohol, nicotine or drugs; although my wayward ways were not quite in that category, I still find it dispiriting.

Cut down *gradually* on your intake of food, bearing in mind what you *used* to eat, and what you can actually get by on. There is a big difference, I can assure you. Simply help yourself to a smaller portion than usual – it may help if you put your portion on a smaller plate where it will look more! An interesting 'for instance' is that steaks usually come in 6–8 oz (175–225 g) weights. The actual bodily *need* per day of that meat protein is only 2–3 oz (50–75 g) so in one meal you could be eating three to four days worth!

It will take you a few weeks to understand that your previous intake was excessive and unnecessary, but you *will* make the breakthrough in a couple of weeks and from then on it is so much easier.

It also occurred to me, at the beginning of my new-found approach to food, eating and living, that whenever I was with company, I was always the first to finish my meal. I have since realised that most people in catering are the same. We have become used to having to snatch a meal on the hop, knowing full well that before we had finished the plate some-body would be wanting something and so the food was never, ever digested.

An old close friend said to me each time I dined in her company that I ate far too fast and would have digestive and weight problems if, like her, I didn't chew each mouthful of food thirty-two times. I tried. There's nothing left by the time I get to twenty-two let alone thirty-two, but this *slower* eating approach can help as much as eating less. The chewing also helps psychologically. The smaller amount of food on your plate can now take the same time to eat, and you won't feel deprived.

To you this may sound like bunkum, but *it worked for me*. Initially it all felt rather silly, but in the second week I realised that I wasn't quite so tense. I was

---

Eat less at each meal: take smaller portions; take smaller mouthfuls; eat more slowly; deliberately leave something on your plate.

relaxing while I ingested, and I felt marvellous at the end of the month. I would never have thought that such a small alteration in eating habits could possibly have such a significant effect on my health and well-being.

When surrounded by food – as I am constantly – I *still* find my right hand starting to reach out for something sinful. It happened when I was writing this piece, and this was after *months* of being good. I went through into the Miller Howe kitchen from the office and saw the first frying of lovely crisp slices of courgette being turned out on to a tray to drain. As my hand was about to pounce, a little voice from somewhere asked:

Does your body really need this?

Does your mind really need this?

And, of course, the answer was quite plainly NO. I resisted the temptation and even the Chef looked at me with eyes uplifted and said 'Good for you, Mr T.'

Never eat when you're not hungry.

Rule No. 4

Cook in a Healthier Way

The healthier ways are boiling, grilling and steaming. Another thing I do quite often is bake meats or veg wrapped in foil, greaseproof or those special oven bags. Anything which uses cooking fat in any quantity is out. That means deep-frying, shallow-frying and roasting.

SAUTÉING

This would seem to be too like fat-frying, but if you buy a good, fairly thick-bottomed non-stick frying-pan you will be agreeably surprised at how you can still sauté most things without any fat at all (although never over a high heat). Or you could just paint the pan with a tiny amount of oil – you will be amazed at just how little can cook so much. A wok is good too – you only need a tiny amount of oil for something like a vegetable stir-fry.

Numerous dishes call for fried onions as their base, and in the past I used to cook them in so much butter and oil they turned a delicious golden colour, rarely brown. Now, using a wooden spoon, you will have to stand over the pan whilst they are frying in no fat, constantly turning them. As they turn brown (the sugar coming out), speed up the stirring, or add a tiny amount of water.

Even the leanest minced meat contains some fat, so you could, if you liked, sauté it first, then drain off the fat before continuing with the recipe. (Or you could *boil* it briefly, drain well, then continue as usual.)

BOILING

Vegetables are cooked in boiling water until just *al dente* or just tender – unless of course they are to be puréed or mashed. Save the cooking water for a soup stock, as many of the nutrients of the veg will have gone into the water.

Some sauce bases can be reduced by boiling – rather as I once reduced cream for my wonderful creamy sauces. For instance, gravies in the past had to be thick and old-fashioned, using flour to thicken them. I still make lots of gravy but it is thin to start off with – some stock and the meat juices – then boiled to reduce to give body and to concentrate flavour.

GRILLING

This is a quick and healthy method of cooking because no extra fat is necessary (as there would be in roasting), and any fat in the food will drop away. Vegetables can be grilled too, but at a lower heat as they will burn more easily.

46

STEAMING

This has become one of my favourite cooking methods since starting to live and eat more healthily. It's a more delicate and controllable process than boiling.

I invested in a two-tier steamer, and I find it invaluable now, using it for meats, fish and vegetables. I use salt in the water and add other flavourings so that the fragrant steam will enhance the food being cooked. Use this water afterwards in some way (if not too salty), as it will contain some vitamins and minerals condensed from the foods (although less are lost in steaming than in boiling).

If you can't find or afford a proper steamer – but I do urge you to buy one, it'll be worth the expense – a colander over a pan of boiling water will suffice, so long as the lid fits well.

Rule No. 5

Concentrate on Flavour

Flavourless foods are boring foods, and this is anathema to the bingeing dieter. Somehow, if something tastes right or delicious, it makes up for any feeling of deprivation, and I've used lots of little 'tricks' in my months of eating less.

The fat in or on meat or poultry makes it cook well and taste good, so I cook meats with the fat still on and then cut it off afterwards. A sirloin steak is moistened by its frill of fat during cooking, but I now cut it off and discard it (into a doggie bag for Ozzie) without a thought. A whole chicken is still roasted with its skin, or a portion grilled, but I then remove the skin before I eat; the flesh will have been flavoured but not saturated by the fat. I often grill calves' liver on or with some bacon just to get the flavour but don't eat the bacon.

I marinate a lot of meats now before cooking, as this gives wonderful flavours as well. I use a mixture of oils and vinegars, wines or citrus juices, and lots of other flavourings, and marinate in airtight containers in the fridge for up to four days. Then I cook the meats at a much higher temperature for a shorter length of time. Even some good mustard spread on a meat before baking adds wonderful flavour.

I also marinate vegetables. For a supper treat,

when I'm by myself, I will marinate for four hours a small selection of finely cut veg (mangetout, celery, carrot and parsnip, for instance) in a light French dressing and then steam them for a matter of minutes, adding lots of freshly chopped herbs. Herbs are a wonderful flavouring too: they can be added to the water of a steamer, chopped on top of foods to be steamed – my new potatoes wouldn't taste so good if I didn't steam them with lashings of fresh mint – and a large sprig or two as a garnish adds colour and fibre as well as flavour. Your taste-buds should tingle with the end results. The use of herbs can also cut down on the need for salt – it is the ultimate food flavouring but one which we are all advised to cut down on. Lovage, a very savoury herb, is particularly good in this respect.

Garlic is a wonderful flavouring in itself, and I would never serve a salad unless the bowl had first been rubbed with a crushed clove. Many spices can also be called upon to give tang and depth of taste.

Even in sandwiches I need to have flavour – thus the cucumber in vinegar and the nigh blackened slices of bread (see p. 98).

> Garlic, like herbs, helps to make foods taste better if you are using less salt.

Rule No. 6

Allow the Occasional Binge

'Home is heaven and orgies are vile,
But you need an orgy, once in a while.'

OGDEN NASH

Herein lies the secret of my success. At the beginning of my 'change of life' attitude towards food I soon realised that if I didn't occasionally go off on a binge I would become the world's worst whinger. I always thought that the world's greatest bore was the one keen on food and wine; I now think it's the born-again dieter! Well, it would be, but I have often strayed from the straight and narrow, and I would be lying if I claimed to have religiously stuck to my new-found way of life 100 per cent.

The first thing I realised was that to deprive yourself of something you wanted made that something seem more desirable. If your mouth, tongue and taste-buds need a particular taste, they must be satisfied. It went back to that fifth day of the *BBC Diet* when I was supposed to have steamed fish and I desired, nay craved, a lamb chop. For me rigid diets have always failed because they do not take into account the actual sensual side of eating.

I started my attempt to shed surplus blubber in March 1990, and in July that year I was due to go on holiday to Morocco with two very close friends who adore food, wine and fellowship. In no way did I wish to cramp their style or endanger the long-standing friendship. In ten days I put on six pounds, but oh what fun we had, what dishes and bottles we lovingly shared. But I would have been much more over the top if I hadn't, unknown to them, practised a lot of self-restraint.

I did eat a lot – breakfast, lunch, tea, dinner – and I drank as much as ever, but cleverly began to understand how to read a menu enabling me to order plenty of food but of dishes devoid of the devil! And in order not to appear anti-social at nibble time, when coaxed by my friends to join them in their ways, I did not appear puritanical at all but bent down to take *one* nut or *one* crisp. As I put it in my mouth I chewed those famous thirty-two times, so they thought I was normal and not holier than thou.

OK, when I got back I *had* put on weight, but in just over two weeks, after a lot of effort, it was all off. I firmly applied my own rules again, and ate salads

If you're a cheese freak and crave flavour, keep some good Parmesan well wrapped in the fridge. When the urge comes upon you, just grate off a level dessertspoon, put some on your damp index finger and slowly let the flavour burst on your taste-buds.

and lean meats – I even cut down on the wine a little. The main thing, however, was that I had enjoyed myself which is, after all, what life is all about.

I clearly recall the next time I went overboard. It was the day my last TV series was launched and we had been invited down to Cardiff to a party given by the seven amateur cooks participating in the show. As we arrived early, I decided that I would treat us all to lunch at a little restaurant close to the BBC which we had enjoyed whilst filming. We were the only guests on a very hot day and, partly out of pity, partly from frustration, I went for the full three-course meal ending up with an enormous piece of the most delicious pavlova I can recall. I actually found myself asking for more cream. Now cream was, truly, something I had avoided for fifteen months, and it was like having a fix. I suddenly realised, foolishly, what I had been missing, and made a pig of myself.

That evening we went on to the marvellous, never-to-be-forgotten party in the country. What a welcome I was given, and what a spread there was before me.

To satisfy my occasional craving for chocolate, I wrap individual segments of a chocolate orange in foil, and freeze them. When the urge comes, I unwrap and slowly suck the rock-hard segment for about 20 minutes. Psychologically, I feel as if I've eaten a pound of Black Magic!

As each and every one of the seven had been beavering away for two days, I had to weigh in and attack the laden buffet table. Everything not only looked wonderful, but tasted superb. I didn't want to upset anybody by not eating a bit of everything, and it was only half an hour before I found myself being as greedy as I used to be. At two o'clock in the morning I realised my mistake, and there followed four sorry hours I would rather erase from my memory. My poor system just couldn't take it after so long without.

I am sure I put on two and half pounds that one evening, but after three days of a fresh fruit and steamed spinach diet, accompanied by apples, carrots and a thick slice of cold beef minus any trace of fat each evening, I lost that extra, *plus* one pound.

This is *not* a way of dieting that I recommend, but it is good to know that I am human and that humans

do invariably err from time to time. If I hadn't allowed myself that binge, I don't think I would have enjoyed myself half as much. You've only got to make up for it, either before or after – your self-punishment if you like. So, if you are going to a wedding, dinner or on holiday, please don't let your new food fads intrude on the *joy*. Remember, food is fun, even when you're on a diet.

A BINGE INGREDIENT

Everyone has got one passion which they would only be able to give up with great difficulty and great pain when dieting. I think you ruddy well *need* that something to maintain your sanity and sustain your determination. My binge ingredient is wine.

Most folk who are authoritative on the subject of diet get really annoyed with me over my approach to the bottle. They look at me in despair, shake their heads and say no, no, no. They seem to think one cannot shed pounds when drinking all those units a day (and I must admit to enjoying my binge passion to the tune of about one to one and a half bottles a day). But I simply look at them with joy, nod my head, and say, look at me, I've lost nearly three stone with the help of wine. I never ask or question how much more I would have lost without it, but I do know that I would have lost my sense of humour and purpose in life.

54

Alcohol is, I know, quite fattening – a glass of dry white wine contains about 90 calories, I believe – and most opponents say that if you have too much your will-power goes and you take to the forbidden foods as well. It hasn't worked like that for me, and I still lose weight while enjoying my crisp and clean New World wines.

I discovered another 'plus' for my chosen binge ingredient in a book called *Wine is the Best Medicine* by Dr E.A. Maury. This makes for fascinating reading, and is balm to my soul. He advises one to two glasses of claret should be drunk with every meal – and if that includes breakfast, lunch, afternoon tea and supper, it means eight glasses are OK by him, only two short of my daily intake of ten!

Seriously, though, he studies not only the grapes used in the making of every wine, but the make-up of the soil and situation of the respective vineyards, and prescribes on that basis: Provençal rosé is good for gout, he says, white Anjou wines for constipation, and champagne for heart disease. Restored by this, I absolutely see to it that I drink a good cross-section of all the wines throughout the course of a month, and reckon I am sensibly hedging my bets and keeping illness at bay. Indeed I hardly ever visit my doctor.

I do truly believe that wine is good for me, and it certainly does wonders for my spirits. This may not be *your* binge choice, and you may not indeed *need* the built-in binge excuse to keep you happy. If so, you are very fortunate, you are stronger willed than most of us. But could you enjoy your slimming diet and life *more* if you let go a bit . . .

If you feel you couldn't cope with *my* binge ingredient, drink mineral water. This has no calories, tastes pleasant, and with a slice of lemon or lime looks much more interesting – like a gin and tonic in fact! Or have a spritzer – half white wine, half soda or mineral water, and half the calories.

Rule No. 7

Take Some Exercise

I have never, ever been athletic. At grammar school, to avoid games, I would nip over the playing fields wall each Wednesday afternoon, walk to the trolley bus-stop, run upstairs and lie down on the floor whilst the vehicle passed the school, then go on to enjoy the matinee at the Theatre Royal. In the Army (where I was part of the Secretariat), I cunningly switched the telex machine *off* about an hour before square bashing was to take place; by switching it on ten minutes before, I could convince my superiors there were too many ABC Bentley coded messages from Headquarters to be decoded.

I had a car from the age of eighteen and drove everywhere when I was in Africa. I did, at one time, belong to the Mlanje Mountain Club in Nyasaland and actually walked up it most weekends (partly for the wonderful suppers we used to cook in the guest huts on the plateau!), but was invariably the first to set off and the last to arrive. In Ghana I became quite

> Just 20 minutes of brisk walking three or four times a week could make the difference between life and death.

expert at outdoor badminton, but no other sport called me. My attempts at tennis were pathetic, and I haven't the eye for billiards.

WALKING

However, ten years ago some Cape Town friends started to take me on relatively gentle walks on Table Mountain, and I discovered the joys of walking. For the whole of January and February, when I winter in the sunny Cape, I am up at half-past five each morning and take dear Matthew with me for a four- to five-hour leisurely walk up on the mountain. This year, coming back from a particularly difficult walk which involved scrambling and nigh climbing in order to see a rare wild flower, we returned to the lovely hotel in Claremont where I stay. My initial concern was for Matthew. I rushed into the kitchen, got a bowl of milk to which I added an egg, a touch of brandy and some icing sugar, and whisked it all up. As I rushed out to give it to Matthew, a guest came to greet me. When I said I had to tend to my dear friend Matthew, he gave me such an odd look. That evening at sun-downer time the owner of the hotel was recalling my stressful morning, much to the raised eyebrows of some of the guests, but all was soon put right when in walked my Matthew, a lovely black cross-bred labrador!

Now at the farm or in Bowness I walk Ozzie and

myself religiously for an hour and a half every day, but I do it at a leisurely pace. A daily route march is not for me. I like to stop and talk to other folk on the walk, or occasionally to sit down and take in the glorious views. I used to find the simplest of excuses to avoid this. I would say to Ozzie, 'You've performed today, so you don't need a long walk'. 'Joe Soap is calling round in half an hour, so we can only go for a stroll.' 'Is that a cloud I can see on the horizon, Ozz? We will get wet.' Now however, it's out in all weathers, protected by our all-weather gear, and it's done wonders for my figure and health.

When travelling I now always make the time to walk to where I am going (I have the energy and eagerness to do so), rather than take taxis. I use the stairs in department stores rather than the lifts and escalators. If the distance to be travelled is long, I take public transport to within a twenty-minute final walk! Even if you live in the middle of the city you can do all this. Initially just walk short distances and don't push yourself. It's all a matter of getting your life organised and being determined to do something about your fatness and fitness.

GYMS

Yes, I too have joined various gym and fitness clubs and been intrigued by all the horrendous, satanic-looking equipment and have been instructed as to how to use this machine for my thigh muscles, that for my tummy. The exercise bike is not for me either, as it's so uncomfortable on one's rear end, and I found it boring, making me uptight and tense. I don't think any sort of fanaticism about exercise and fitness is the answer for most of us.

At one time I belonged to an excellent club in Windermere, and went every single day, but it was the jacuzzi and the superb massage that were the carrot before the donkey. I love being massaged by firm hands, and the lady there certainly left me in no doubt whatsoever that she was getting well and truly down to breaking up the nodules of fat in my unhealthy body.

SWIMMING

I have osteo-arthritis, and a few years ago my specialist said I should take up swimming. I did. I mortgaged my pensions and built a swimming pool at the farm and now do about thirty lengths first thing in the morning and in the early evening. (I've worked up to that gradually.) Everyone said it would be a five-day wonder and that I would soon give up. I have proved them wrong and often find myself doing thirty-five to forty lengths at each session. It has undoubtedly helped my figure, and I do believe it has helped my arthritis. If there is a swimming pool en route to your place of work, couldn't you possibly find thirty minutes a day for this form of exercise?

STRETCHING AND RELAXING

When I was about four weeks into the diet and getting on target, I must admit there were days that I felt extremely tired after work. Some folk said because I wasn't stoking my body and brain with enough food (and by food they meant all the things I thought I couldn't do without!), I would soon be run down and become ill. I then remembered that in one of the health farms I'd visited years before, a lot of emphasis was put on some simple stretching exercises to be done morning and night. I started doing them as I watched breakfast TV (instead of lolling on the bed playing with Ozzie), and late at night when I usually get down to reading the day's newspaper.

The first exercise always allows me to get a good night's sleep. Place two pillows on the floor close to your bed in such a position that you can lay your head and tops of your shoulders on them. Arch your body up on to the bed with your legs lying on top of it. Stretch your arms out as far as possible on either side of your shoulders. Keep your eyes open as wide as possible and concentrate hard on a set place on the ceiling (I've stuck some large luminous nursery stars above the bed). Start taking very deep breaths, hold your breath and then slowly breathe out. Do this for five minutes at first, then for longer. I find myself becoming relaxed and slightly drowsy, it's a delightful feeling.

After a particularly bad day when I'm mentally on a high, I no longer resort to a sleeping tablet. By opening my mouth as far as possible, this induces long yawns and very soon my eyelids begin to come closer together. There's nothing terribly clever or scientific about this, but it works!

Years ago, when flying was fraught and the air-lines were there for the convenience of the crew rather than the paying passengers, British Airways had on their in-flight entertainment a series of tension-freeing exercises that could be done whilst you were hunched up in your seat, with hardly an inch to manoeuvre in any direction. Having eaten the plastic stodge to relieve the boredom on trans-atlantic flights, at any given moment you could see half the passengers thrusting their necks in an upwards position like crowing cockerels! You knew that they, like you, were practising the exercises!

I find nowadays that, whatever I am doing (putting my hand up to the shelf above this computer to bring down a book, say) I make a point of over-extending the movement and doing it rather more slowly than

62

usual. This is good and stretchy. When sitting working at the word processor, watching the box or reading, from time to time I lift my legs from the knees downwards and pedal as if I am on a bike. When out walking I am forever slowly but positively turning my neck from left to right, but going as far in each direction as possible. You feel the initial slight strain, but stretching the muscles is a good thing. Having become aware of how much improved my arthritis is because of these little points, I find myself doing the exercises in the most peculiar places: during intervals at the theatre; whilst waiting for a course in a restaurant; standing in a queue at the post office . . .

It is well known that daily workouts increase your metabolism, and tend to curb your appetite as well. My forms of exercise would hardly be deemed 'workouts', but they have got me moving, toned me up, and thinned me down. I hope the same can happen to you.

Binge Diet Weight Loss

It would be silly of me to encourage *you* to take up all my habits. I have simply recorded what and how I am now eating and drinking compared with what I once did. If I, surrounded by all the good things in life, can lose nearly three stone over a period of two years, and keep it off, so too can you.

Common sense and patience will do it. Never hurry it. A stone in weight will not disappear in two weeks, and to do it so fast is foolish. I know people who have lost about sixteen pounds in this period, but their systems went into shock, and they very quickly put it all back on. Shell-shock and complacency can be disastrous.

When you start your new serious approach to living, make a note on the calendar, or in your diary or filofax, what your weight is. Do this stark naked after performing your ablutions. One week later, and not before, repeat the procedure. Don't be like me at the beginning and go on the ruddy scale morning, noon and night. It becomes a fix, and your mental attitude goes up and down like your weight. It can be very depressing.

Initially you could possibly shed three pounds in the first week, and you should feel duly proud of yourself. Thereafter though, aim for a gradual one and a half pounds reduction every single week. This allows you to cheat occasionally or dine out, and is fairly painless. Needless to say, I didn't succeed each and every week, as I had my weekend breaks, holidays and binges, but I soon made it up.

Occasionally, when I have been in the company of learned folk, and the subject of my diet has come up, I feel quite freakish when I start to describe my new approach to eating. I often get involved in quite heated argument – particularly about the drink question. However, I simply have to shake my head, acknowledge their wisdom, but quietly say: 'I am sure you are absolutely right, but this has worked for me, and the proof of the pudding is in my slimmer body and better medical . . .'

I truly do know that practically anyone can shed the pounds I have, and keep them off. I am surrounded by food day in and day out, but I am no longer tempted. Virtuous I am not, but practical I am.

CHAPTER 2

EVERYDAY
EATING

Now that you have digested the rules – such as they are – of my ideas on losing weight, we can consider how to eat for the rest of your life. In the following chapters I give ideas for special occasions – when entertaining at home, when eating out at restaurants or with friends – but here we deal with the majority of your meals, those eaten every day. It's easy enough to blame a special occasion for a sudden increase in poundage, but that comes only every so often, and it's much more likely to be controlled by what you take in on a daily basis. This, then, is where I think most of your effort should be aimed.

Breakfasts

I must admit first of all to eating very little first thing in the day as I am used to having my main meal in the evening due to the demands of my profession. If your metabolism works the other way round, however, you will need to start your day with something after the long overnight fast. In fact, I believe that research has shown that schoolchildren and other workers who go without breakfast are said to be less efficient and less mentally alert. And, for most

> Spread a stick of celery with some cottage cheese for a quick snack if you're hungry.

68

people, it is better to eat sparingly at three or so meals per day, then to blow out (albeit modestly) at one, which is what I seem to do. *Balance* out the day's intake: if you eat quite a bit at breakfast, eat less at the other meals. And remember too, to cut down on what you might normally take – by chewing longer you will soon be thinking you have had as much as you used to.

FRUIT

I always start every day with a glass of freshly squeezed lemon juice, then wait for about an hour before I have another bite (if indeed I *choose* to have a bite). Or I might have a vegetable juice instead of anything else (see p. 130). I could have a bowl of fresh grapefruit segments; somehow, prepared this way, I think grapefruit is more appealing, and I prefer it to tearing out shreds and fibre from the halved skin itself. Other fresh fruit could be enjoyed – perhaps as a fresh fruit salad (see p. 129) with yoghurt and a few toasted sunflower seeds on top. When in season, I will have quite a few fresh whole raspberries; if you purée them, the seeds make the mixture bitter, so

The 'raiding-the-fridge syndrome' starts in the supermarket. Don't *buy* anything that will become temptation.

69

you have to add sugar. I could have a small bowl of prunes, or dried fruit compote (see p. 128).

CEREALS

Most commercial cereals contain quite substantial proportions of sugar and salt, so should be avoided. Even the most famous bran cereal contains 1 teaspoon of sugar per bowlful – so think what the ones coated in cocoa or sugar contain (up to and over 3 teaspoons per bowl). The sole sugar-free commercial cereal is, I believe, the one only super athletes can eat three of . . .

I might choose to have a bowl of muesli which I mix up myself (many commercial mueslis contain sugar). Home-made muesli is full of fibre and goodness, and with some yoghurt or skimmed milk, perhaps with some added fresh fruit, it makes a very satisfying start to the day. Buy a cereal base at the health-food shop – wheat, barley, oats, rye etc – then add some bran (wheat *and* oat) and anything else that takes your fancy: a few nuts (not *too* many), seeds and/or dried fruit. (The latter will give you the sweetness your body might desire.) Store in an

---

Instead of an apple pie, try a baked apple with some natural yoghurt and perhaps a few raisins.

---

air-tight jar so that you have it handy for every day.

Another possibility is a small bowl of porridge, made with medium or coarse oats soaked overnight and cooked in skimmed milk or water. Oats have been proved to be good in controlling cholesterol levels. Oat bran is particularly good for this so include some of that in the mixture as well.

COOKED DISHES

The simplest would be a toasted piece of muesli bread, which I might spread with a home-made fruit purée (see p. 74). Marmite soldiers are another not-too-fattening delight. My favourite, though, is muesli bread toast topped with two sliced or halved tomatoes baked in the oven until slightly mushy: I transfer these, with their juices, to the toast and liberally coat them with freshly ground black pepper.

I seldom have guests for breakfast, but if I did, then I would binge modestly alongside them with *one* rasher of grilled lean bacon and a poached egg (I'd have to bear that in mind for the rest of the day though, balancing out my intake). One soft-boiled egg to their two is a possibility too. Or I might serve my guests cold roast ham with a wedge of local farmhouse Lancashire cheese: I would have a smidgen of both with a tomato. Smoked haddock poached in skimmed milk with a few onion circles, a sprig of parsley and black peppercorns isn't too dangerous for me: it's a considerable improvement on the rich cheese sauce I used to envelop the haddock in and then present in puff pastry vol-au-vents or butter-baked cob containers!

MUESLI BREAD

I used to be a breadaholic. As soon as I smelled bread coming out of the main kitchen oven – no matter what time of day – I had to be in there to do a bit of 'quality control'. There is nothing, but nothing, to compare with the smell of freshly baked yeast bread or buns, which are then split open, steaming hot, and lathered with good butter. It's food for the gods or, as it used to be, for the fatties! I honestly thought I would never be able to give bread up, but I concocted the following recipe which I have toasted for breakfast or spread with a fruit purée for afternoon tea. It is a bastardised version of the famous Miller Howe wholemeal bread, but it is decidedly delicious and definitely part of my new way of eating. It's truly a bread I could 'die' for!

MAKES 3 × 1 lb (450 g) LOAVES
4 oz (100 g) oats
8 oz (225 g) Jordan's crunchy oats
4 oz (100 g) shelled hazelnuts, coarsely chopped
1 lb (450 g) wholemeal flour (do not sieve!)
2 heaped tablespoons caraway seeds
4 oz (100 g) sultanas

2 oz (50 g) dried banana flakes, crushed
1 teaspoon salt
1 tablespoon mixed spice
4 tablespoons runny honey
1¼ pints (750 ml) warm water
2½ oz (65 g) fresh yeast
10 fl oz (300 ml) plain yoghurt
2 tablespoons each of poppy and sesame seeds

Lightly grease three 1 lb (450 g) loaf tins.

Mix the first nine ingredients in a large mixing bowl and put in a warm, draught-free place.

In a smaller bowl, mix the honey with 5 fl oz (150 ml) of the warm water (straight from the hot tap will do). On top of this break up the fresh yeast and place, once again, somewhere warm, where it can be cared for – nay, cosseted – until the yeast looks like the delicious head on a glass of Guinness.

Add the remaining warm water to the yeast bowl and pour on to the dry ingredients. Add the yoghurt and, using a long-handled spoon, mix all the ingredients together.

Spread half of the poppy and sesame seeds on the bases of the greased loaf tins. Divide the clarty mixture between the tins, knock down and then sprinkle the balance of the seed mixture on top.

Put the three tins on a baking tray and cover them with a piece of dampened greaseproof paper. Leave once again in the same warm place until the mix has virtually doubled in size, about 30 minutes.

Meanwhile, pre-heat the oven to gas mark 6, 400°F (200°C). Bake the loaves for 45 minutes, remove from the oven and leave to go cold. Slice thickly and toast, preferably under a very hot grill, to make the bread go very crisp and slightly burnt. It is so sweet and so full of flavour that you can simply eat it as it is for breakfast. (You don't *really* need butter or jam or marmalade.) In fact I feel it sets me up for the day!

BINGE DIET 'JAMS'

In the old days my breakfast toast was literally smothered with lots of lovely butter and either home-made marmalade or lemon curd. Nowadays I simply spread on to the unbuttered slices a purée made from, say, a couple of apples or pears. I peel, core and finely slice these, and then simmer them with the juice and rind of a half lemon. I find that most fruits respond to this method. Or I could just mash up a ripe plum, peach or nectarine, or raspberries or strawberries. I might put some low fat yoghurt on top with a sprinkling of toasted seeds. Sometimes (particularly with rhubarb) I add a teaspoon of the Curry Essence on p. 88 when cooking. I always liquidise the end result and pass it through a sieve to make a nursery-style baby-food mix. You will be agreeably surprised to note just how sweet fresh fruit are when cooked in this way, and no sugar is required whatsoever.

Salads

I occasionally despair when I'm out shopping and see folks buying a lettuce, some boiled beetroot, spring onions and a bit of cucumber, and thinking that that's their lot for a salad. How many working people come home to be faced with a plate of these terribly basic (good, I'll admit) but boring items along with a slice of bought tinned ham or tongue? There's so much more to salads than that, and if there wasn't, many more people would be unable to stick to any diet.

Naturally enough, salads should form a major proportion of your dietary lifestyle, which is why I've given them a section all of their own. It is well known that raw vegetables and fruit are good for us, retaining their full complement of vitamins, minerals and fibre. Most of them are also low in calories. I like salads with *lots* of ingredients and once revelled in bowlfuls rich in additions such as croûtons and nuts. These are out now to a great extent, although a little of the Pesto Crisp on p. 84 or a *few* chopped nuts can't do any harm occasionally. The flavour and texture will add so much to your pleasure.

Keep some peeled or scrubbed raw carrots handy in the fridge to nibble on between meals.

A few months ago I was filming a 30-minute documentary with the BBC as part of a series called *The Happiest Days of Your Life*. When the film crew arrived at the farm mid-morning it was decided that rather than do a straightforward, sit-down, face-to-face interview I would stand at my usual work-place in the kitchen and bring together a large bowl of salad. (Very clever thinking on the part of the director, as we could then all devour this for our late lunch!) I scratched around in my fridges, and went over to my lovely neighbours who have a fantastic smallholding (the four of them are virtually self-sufficient all year round).

It was a frantic 20 minutes as I started to gather up endless ingredients on the work-top and in the side sinks. The lights were switched on, the sound double-checked and the camera started to roll. I started by wiping the inside of a large round dish with a little hazelnut oil and then pressed a crushed clove of garlic all over. Just over an hour later (no double takes needed, but we had to stop once to reload the cassette and replace the batteries), we had the interview literally 'in the can' and I had before me a *mountainous*, truly mind-boggling salad.

We sat down and ate it with a large pea and aspic herbed slice using the Chicken Jelly Dressing on p. 82 with orange and mint. It was one of those feasts that are memorable purely and simply for their straightforward simplicity.

Remember I was using *left-overs* and odds and ends; the following list details them in the order of build-up. Some ingredients are not to be used *too* generously when you're dieting, though.

fresh spinach
finely sliced iceberg lettuce
watercress leaves
mustard and cress
lean cubed bacon, fried off in a little walnut oil (go easy on this)
hard-boiled eggs, peeled and pushed through a sieve
salted honey peanuts (go easy on these)
very generous amount of freshly chopped herbs
garden peas
broad beans, lightly cooked and skinned
cooked French beans and baby sweetcorn from the night before, finely chopped
apple wedges soaked in fresh lime juice
thinly sliced mangetout
grated carrot
cherry tomatoes
grated courgette with a touch of grated orange rind
chive, marjoram and nasturtium flowers
toasted sunflower seeds
Pesto Crisp (see p. 84)

If salads are to become a part of your new way of eating – as they should be – then you have to put a little effort and lots of imagination into them. The only thing that isn't called for is skill.

Salad ingredients are obviously better and more readily available in warmer weather but supermarkets these days come up with some remarkable bags of mixed greens. The boxes of growing herbs are a boon too.

Most salad greens are spotlessly clean but if you are fortunate enough to grow your own then you will have to wash them in cold water. Invest in a salad spinner (they are a *must*) as in no time whatsoever all the damp, clean greens will be as dry as bone and quite crisp too. If you are using fresh spinach, it is essential you strip the green leaf from the rather tough, bitter stalk.

Many old cookery books say quite emphatically that salad greens must never be cut with a knife, but that they should be torn into pieces. I don't agree. I cut an iceberg lettuce into four wedges and then finely cut it into very thin strips.

Broad beans – sadly, available only for a short period in the summer – have to be taken out of their pods, lightly cooked in simmering salted water, and then strained. Run cold water over them to cool them down. You then have to sit down and painstakingly pop each bright green bean out of its skin. Well worth the effort.

If possible, avoid peeling carrots as there is so much flavour in the skin. Scrub them instead. I always have a couple of sticks of celery and two carrots soaking in cold water in an airtight container in the fridge. They are marvellous to stave off pangs of hunger and are so much better for you than a chocolate bar.

It is, however, watercress that I buy most of these days, and I seldom make any salad without it because of its strong peppery flavour. I agree it never quite tastes so good as it did in my youth when it was picked fresh from streams running through woods, tied into bunches with coarse brown string, and then brought round the back streets strapped to the handlebars of a bike in a large leather pouch similar to a postman's delivery bag. Nowadays it is farmed extensively rather than grown naturally by Mother Nature. I always remember the year we could no longer go out in the Lakes and pick it from the sides of streams. The Ministry of Agriculture had decreed that the sheep might have foot-rot or there could be chemicals in the streams from insecticides spread on the land. God knows what it must have cost to take up *all* the beds of watercress from *all* the streams. But that is called progress . . .

If you are like me, you will find that your taste-buds become much cleaner and more demanding as you cease simply stuffing grub in your gob! So salads these days are festooned, nigh plastered, with freshly chopped garden herbs. Parsley is available throughout the year, and is a good base, but go for dill, fennel, chives, tarragon, mint and be sparing with lovage (a very dominant flavour). My personal favourite has to be basil, and I also make a very good sauce and salad addition with it (see pp. 84 and 162).

The following salads are a few combinations I particularly like: all serve four, and the weights given are *prepared* weights. Wash everything well and dry thoroughly. Dress with one of the dressings starting on p. 81.

3 oz (75 g) spinach, stalks and middle vein removed
1 bunch watercress
1 punnet mustard and cress
6 spring onions, trimmed and finely cut
1 hard-boiled egg, shelled and rubbed through a fine sieve
8 radishes, trimmed and finely grated

3 oz (75 g) spinach, stalks and middle vein removed
¼ iceberg lettuce, finely shredded
4 oz (100 g) white button mushrooms, wiped and thinly sliced
2 nectarines or peaches, stoned and cut into small wedges
3 oz (75 g) red pepper, de-seeded and thinly sliced

½ iceberg lettuce, finely shredded
4 oz (100 g) fresh shelled broad beans, partly cooked
2 oz (50 g) fresh uncooked garden peas
20 mint leaves, finely chopped with a little sugar and salt
1 large apple, cored and finely chopped

⅓ iceberg lettuce, finely shredded
8 oz (225 g) baby courgettes, wiped and grated
finely grated rind of 2 oranges
5 in (13 cm) medium thick cucumber, chopped
sprigs from 1 bunch watercress

½ iceberg lettuce, finely shredded
1 red onion, peeled and finely cut into circles, then
marinated for 1 hour in a little raspberry vinegar
3 oranges, peeled and segmented
1 punnet mustard and cress

HERB DRESSING

*This would be good served with sturdier salads – those
made with endive, chicory, spinach, etc.*

MAKES ABOUT 10 fl oz (300 ml)
10 fl oz (300 ml) Greek yoghurt
2 oz (50 g) chopped fresh herbs
2 teaspoons lemon juice
½ garlic clove, peeled, crushed and mixed to a paste with
1 level teaspoon made English mustard

Simply mix together in a bowl. Use fairly swiftly.

MUSTARD AND ORANGE DRESSING

This may taste a little sweet for some, but I find it wonderful with stronger tasting salad leaves such as watercress.

MAKES ABOUT 7 fl oz (200 ml)
4 fl oz (120 ml) sunflower oil
2 fl oz (50 ml) cider vinegar
juice and finely grated zest of 1 orange
salt and freshly ground black pepper
1 teaspoon runny honey
2 teaspoons coarse-grain mustard

Simply combine everything in a screw-top jar and shake thoroughly together.

CHICKEN JELLY DRESSING

When you roast a chicken, save the fat and juices from the butter or bacon used to protect and moisten the bird, and the juices of the bird itself. These juices will separate and solidify, leaving a wonderfully flavoured jelly at the base and removable fat at the top. These jellied juices can be used in a sauce or stock, but are delicious in a salad dressing. Only make a little at a time, as it will not last very long.

MAKES ABOUT 3 fl oz (85 ml)

3 tablespoons olive or sunflower oil, according to taste
3 tablespoons chicken jelly, quickly melted
1 scant tablespoon balsamic vinegar
½ tablespoon very finely chopped fresh herbs (optional)
salt and freshly ground black pepper

Simply mix together well, and use up quickly.

LEMON DRESSING

This is ideal for many of the lighter textured salads in the preceding pages. You could leave out the dry white wine if you like, but the flavour is good – and you will only be ingesting a tiny amount of it.

MAKES ABOUT 6 fl oz (175 ml)

2 tablespoons fresh lemon juice
2 tablespoons dry white wine
8 tablespoons olive oil
1 garlic clove, peeled and crushed with ½ teaspoon runny salt
½ teaspoon dry English mustard powder
1 teaspoon runny honey
a pinch of caster sugar

Simply whizz all ingredients together in the liquidiser. Store in a screw-top jar until ready to use.

PESTO CRISP

Use these highly flavoured nuggets instead of croûtons in salads. Toss on top of the salad after it has been dressed.

4 oz (100 g) Pesto Sauce (see p. 162)
4 oz (100 g) fresh wholemeal breadcrumbs

Pre-heat oven to gas mark 6, 400°F (200°C). Melt the sauce gently, add breadcrumbs and mix well. Turn into a shallow ovenproof container approximately 7 in (18 cm) square. Spread evenly and press down. Bake for 20 minutes. Allow to cool then break into half-walnut-sized pieces. Store in a jar in the fridge.

CARAWAY CHEESE TOASTS

Caraway seeds help the digestion of the cheese, as well as add a wonderful flavour. Serve with a salad.

4 slices thick wholemeal bread
4 oz (100 g) good Cheddar or Lancashire cheese, grated
1 teaspoon caraway seeds
1 egg
1 teaspoon made English mustard

Toast one side of the bread. Mix the cheese, seeds, egg and mustard together, then spread on to the untoasted side. Grill until brown and bubbling.

Lunches and Suppers

The recipes here are, on the whole, adaptations of tried and tested favourites, but restyled to be healthier and less fattening, using less damaging ingredients. A number of them are ever so slightly binge-biased: I would usually advise avoiding pastry dishes, for instance, but a quiche is *so* useful that I've reworked both the pastry *and* the custard. Slimmers should just have a smaller wedge and more salad – a mode of eating to be followed with all the dishes in this section.

I've included a few sweet dessert ideas – and there are more in Chapter Three – but these too are a trifle binge-like: it's always better to stick to plain fruit. However, a little treat every now and again is certainly not unknown in my dietary philosophy!

TOVEY'S BINGE BROTH

I used to adore those thick, croûton-laden, cream-topped, home-made soups and thought I couldn't give them up. However, I now proudly serve 'broths' all the time, dolloping the guests' helpings with crème fraîche, *but mine just scattered with chopped herbs. You could also add a tablespoon of dry sherry to your guests' helpings but restrain yourself from such indulgences!*

If, like me, you're making your own vegetable juices, use the gunge leftover in the juicer container to add flavour to the stock (see p. 131). And to make a vegetable stock, simply omit the chicken carcass; you could add additional flavourings such as peppercorns, bay leaves, etc.

MAKES 2 pints (1.2 litres)

Chicken stock

1 chicken carcass
2 leeks, trimmed (about 6 oz/175 g)
1 small swede (about 12 oz/350 g), peeled
3 carrots (about 8 oz/225 g), peeled
1 onion (about 6 oz/175 g), peeled
**1 container of vegetable 'gunge' from the juicer container
(or *more* vegetable flavourings)**

Broth

6 oz (175 g) root vegetables per person
1 heaped dessertspoon mixed chopped herbs per person
salt and freshly ground black pepper

To make the stock, break up the chicken carcass and put in a large, heavy-bottomed saucepan. (Try never to serve the wings of a chicken, as they make *such* a difference to this stock.) Chop the stock vegetables roughly and add to the pan with enough water to cover. Allow 1 in (2.5 cm) at the top. Cover and simmer – *never boil* – for 3 hours.

Add the leftover vegetable gunge from the juicer (or other flavourings) along with a further 2 pints (1.2 litres) water. Simmer slowly for a further 3 hours. Strain when it has cooled a little, and you will have just over 2 pints (1.2 litres) of the richest, tastiest stock ever.

To make the broth, simply peel and finely dice the requisite amount of root vegetables, and cook off lightly in the stock. Season to taste, and serve in hot soup bowls garnished with the herbs.

Occasionally, I measure out about 5 fl oz (150 ml) of the stock and thin it down with a similar amount of water and heat it up with a touch of Worcestershire sauce to enjoy at elevenses!

For slimming sauces, use reduced meat juices, stock or fruit juice, or puréed fruit (without sugar) or yoghurt.

CURRY ESSENCE

Since being on a diet, I find my tastebuds have become more sharp and alert. Thus, I regret to say, I resort to a recipe which may be familiar to many of you already. This is my own home-made curry 'paste' which is wonderfully tasty, and adds immense flavour to an enormous variety of dishes: try it in curries obviously, but also in dressings as on p. 115, and in soups and vegetable dishes.

MAKES ABOUT 8 fl oz (250 ml)

3 tablespoons olive oil
4 oz (100 g) onions, peeled and finely chopped
2 garlic cloves, peeled and crushed with 1 teaspoon salt
½ teaspoon ground allspice
2 bay leaves
seeds from 3 cardamom pods
2 × 1 inch (2.5 cm) cinnamon sticks
4 cloves
1 tablespoon coriander seeds
1 teaspoon chilli powder
1 teaspoon mustard seeds
6 black peppercorns
1 teaspoon ground turmeric
5 fl oz (150 ml) red wine
2 tablespoons apricot jam

Heat the oil in a pan and fry the onions until golden. Add the garlic and all the spices, and cook over a high heat for a few minutes. Stir well, then add the wine and jam. Simmer for 5 minutes, then cool a little. Remove the cinnamon sticks. Liquidise then pass through a sieve. Store in a screw-top jar in the refrigerator.

OAT PASTRY

This savoury and textured pastry is good to use for quiche bases. Be sure to use what used to be called wheatmeal (not wholemeal) flour; this is sometimes labelled 81 or 85%, or simply coarse brown or farmhouse flour.

MAKES 1 QUICHE
3 oz (75 g) butter, sunflower margarine or similar
3 oz (75 g) rolled oats
3 oz (75 g) wheatmeal flour (see above)
3 oz (75 g) self-raising flour
⅓ level teaspoon salt
1 large egg, to bind

Rub the fat into the oats, flours and salt in a large bowl. Bind with the egg. Bring together gently, and don't over-handle. Chill in the fridge for a couple of hours, then bring back to room temperature before rolling.

Roll out fairly thinly and use to line a loose-bottomed 9–10 in (23–25 cm) quiche tin. It may well break and crack, but the pastry 'patches' well. Line with foil, making sure it covers the pastry rim, put in baking beans and chill again for an hour or so.

Pre-heat the oven to gas mark 4, 350°F (180°C). Place the tin and pastry in the oven and bake blind for 20 minutes. Cool, then fill and bake as below.

QUICHE CUSTARDS

Among my most famous recipes are my quiches – savoury buttery pastry cases filled with a variety of fillings and held together by a double cream and egg custard. As a wedge of quiche is so useful as a starter or as a lunch with a salad, I started experimenting to see whether I could invent a slimmer version. I came up with a pastry (see above) and three custards which are a little less creamy and fattening.

My basic recipe, which filled a 9–10 in (23–25 cm) pastry case, included 2 eggs, 1 egg yolk, seasonings and 10 fl oz (300 ml) double cream. These were simply mixed together and used with the chosen filling, then baked in the pastry case in an oven pre-heated to gas mark 5, 375°F (190°C) for 35 minutes.

For the filling, choose from 8–12 oz (225–350 g) of vegetables, raw or lightly cooked, or flakes or small pieces of meat or fish. Some suggestions might be cauliflower florets with olives and cheese, broad beans with red peppers, onions with bacon, defrosted prawns with flaked almonds, or smoked haddock. Use your imagination, then use one of the following, low-fat custard alternatives.

3 eggs
5 fl oz (150 ml) skimmed milk
salt, black pepper and nutmeg

2 eggs
1 egg yolk
10 fl oz (300 ml) *crème fraîche*
salt, black pepper and nutmeg

2 eggs
1 egg yolk
5 fl oz (150 ml) skimmed milk
5 fl oz (150 ml) *crème fraîche*
salt, black pepper and nutmeg

Use fruit or vegetable 'containers' as an alternative to pastry – for instance bake a quiche filling inside a beef tomato, red pepper or scooped-out onion half.

WATERCRESS, ORANGE, PEA AND MINT SALAD

I find I am using watercress more and more as the base for most of my salads these days, so experiment as much as you can. Grapefruit or orange segments with a few nuts go well with it, as do grated carrots, apples and celeriac. Instead of a French dressing, I occasionally simply soft-boil a couple of free-range farm eggs; I then shell and cut them coarsely, and dribble them over the salad. A final touch is a liberal dousing with freshly ground black pepper.

SERVES 6

1 × 6 oz (175 g) packet frozen *petits pois*
salt and caster sugar to taste
4 bunches fresh watercress (use only the flower ends and cut off the thick base stalks)
3 oranges, peeled and segmented
30 fresh mint leaves, finely chopped
about 3 fl oz (85 ml) Lemon Dressing (see p. 83)

Cook the peas with a little salt and sugar, according to the instructions on the packet. Drain and cool.

Wash the prepared watercress lightly and then carefully pat dry with a tea-towel. Scatter on to the base of your serving dish (I like to use a glass trifle bowl). Combine the other salad ingredients at the last moment and not until immediately prior to serving do you toss in the dressing.

STUFFED AVOCADO WITH LEEKS AND STRAWBERRIES

Having spent my earlier years in Central Africa where avocados were twelve for a ticky (threepenny bit), I became accustomed to them for breakfast, lunch, dinner or supper. So much so, when I started to cut down on my food intake I thought it would be tricky to leave this fruit out, as many dieticians say it is extremely fattening.
I found that by preparing it the following way and having it seldom *rather than* often *I did not put on a single gram!*

SERVES 6 AS A STARTER

2 leeks, trimmed

salt

3 ripe avocados

juice and rind of 1 lemon

1 tablespoon olive oil

6 oz (175 g) low-fat cream cheese

1 tablespoon chopped fresh herbs of choice

1 garlic clove, peeled and crushed

Salad
6 asparagus stalks, well trimmed

6 large iceberg lettuce leaves

12 strawberries, halved

5 fl oz (150 ml) French dressing, including 1 teaspoon raspberry vinegar

94

Cut the leeks in half along their length and poach in simmering salted walter until very soft (about 8 minutes) Refresh in cold water, drain and leave to cool. Separate into strips.

For the salad cook the asparagus in boiling water until just done (about 6 minutes, depending on the thickness) refresh, drain and leave to cool. Cut each stalk *lengthways* into four pieces.

Cut the avocados in half, and remove the stones and skin. Paint the flesh with lemon juice and olive oil to prevent it turning brown.

Mix the cheese with the herbs and garlic, and divide the mixture between the hollows of the avocado halves. Wrap each stuffed half in the cool, steamed leek strips.

Arrange the lettuce leaves on a large platter with the asparagus lengths and the strawberries. Sprinkle with the raspberry-flavoured dressing, and arrange the wrapped avocado halves on top.

Every now and again, go on a one-day fruit or vegetable only diet. This cleans out the system, and gives your body a rest.

HOME-MADE TOMATO HERB SAUCE

This is very useful, primarily because it is so full of flavour. It can top baked potatoes, pasta or brown rice, and accompany hot or cold meats, steamed fish or fish cakes. I like basil best, but you can choose any herb you like. Fresh is best, but if you have no choice, use half the specified quantity of dried.

SERVES 8 GENEROUSLY

3 tablespoons olive oil
4 garlic cloves, peeled and crushed
6 oz (175 g) onions, peeled and finely chopped
2 lb (900 g) tomatoes, plum or beef, quartered
5 fl oz (150 ml) cooking sherry or chicken stock
salt and freshly ground black pepper
1 tablespoon soft brown sugar (if it needs it, it all depends on the tomatoes)
at least 2 tablespoons chopped fresh herbs

Heat the oil in a pan, add the garlic and onion, and cook for 10 minutes. Add the tomatoes (seeds, skin and all) and all the remaining ingredients. Cook slowly, uncovered, for 30–45 minutes, giving it a stir every now and again. Pass through a coarse sieve. Serve hot *or* cold.

BAKED SHALLOTS WITH CORIANDER (OR GINGER)

These are splendid served hot or cold, and make an excellent accompaniment for many dishes.

SERVES 4–6

8 oz (225 g) small shallots (about 24), peeled
2 tablespoons cooking oil

a very generous sprinkling of freshly ground coriander seeds (or a whole kernel of preserved ginger in syrup, very finely diced)

Pre-heat the oven to gas mark 4, 350°F (180°C).

In an ovenproof dish approximately 7 × 5 inches (18 × 13 cm) heat the oil, then sauté the prepared shallots for 5 minutes. Add the coriander (or preserved ginger) and bake in the pre-heated oven for 15 minutes. Serve hot or leave to cool.

Always sit down to eat. It has been proved that eating a snack while absorbed in other things has little effect in satisfying hunger. We need time to chew and enjoy the sensation of eating.

97

Sandwich Snacks

Although we all think sandwiches are fattening, bread is important in any diet, primarily because of its fibre content. My answer to the sandwich problem is to use only one slice of bread, to have an *open* sandwich. If you ate this with a knife and fork, along with a crisp salad, you would have a fairly satisfying – and delicious – snack lunch or supper.

One of the main dietary secrets is that you don't spread any butter on the bread or toast of a sandwich. There are low-fat alternatives if you like them, but there are plenty of other ideas. For a cold pork sandwich, for instance, I would spread the bread base first with a little apple sauce. Puréed cooked gooseberries would be good for lamb. You'll find a few other suggestions here.

As flavour is one of the main necessities in a diet, I tend to make my sandwiches with bread that I have grilled to very dark, nigh black. (I use oval granary loaves which I cut at home into medium slices, but any wholemeal or wheatmeal bread will do.)

In all the following recipes, to serve four, four slices of bread are toasted until very dark, then topped with the varying toppings. Use salt sparingly, black pepper generously.

AVOCADO AND MUSHROOM TOAST TOPPING

Although avocadoes are high in fat and calories, they contain 'good' fat and protein, and are so delicious and satisfying.

2 small or 1 large ripe avocado
4 tomatoes, skinned, de-seeded and finely diced
2 oz (50 g) white button mushrooms, wiped and very finely sliced
1 tablespoon chopped fresh parsley

Mash the avocado until smooth, then spread over the toast. Top in the middle with the tomato dice, and arrange the thin mushroom slices around the edges. Garnish with the parsley.

MUSHROOM AND EGG TOAST TOPPING

4 heaped teaspoons Greek yoghurt
4 oz (100 g) white button mushrooms, wiped and very finely sliced
1 fl oz (25 ml) light French dressing
1 hard-boiled egg, shelled
1 tablespoon chopped fresh parsley

Put a dollop of yoghurt in the middle of each slice of toast, then surround with the thin mushroom slices which have been tossed in the dressing. Sieve the egg over the top and sprinkle with the parsley.

TOMATO, CUCUMBER AND ONION TOAST TOPPING

4 heaped teaspoons Greek yoghurt
2 tomatoes, skinned, de-seeded and finely diced
¼ cucumber, very thinly sliced
2 hard-boiled eggs, shelled
8 spring onions, trimmed and thinly sliced

Put a dollop of yoghurt on each slice and spread it out. Top this with the tomato dice, then the cucumber slices. Slice the eggs, and arrange these on top of the cucumber. Sprinkle with the spring onion.

SARDINE TOAST TOPPING

2 × 4½ oz (120 g) cans of sardines in oil
8 spring onions, trimmed and thinly sliced
1 tablespoon chopped fresh parsley

Drain the sardines, and put a little of the oil on each slice of bread. Arrange the sardines on top, head to tail. Sprinkle with spring onion and parsley.

Green vegetables are at their nutritious best when fresh and lightly steamed to preserve the Vitamin C.

SALMON TOAST TOPPING

1 × 7½ oz (212 g) can of salmon
1 tablespoon *fromage frais*
¼ cucumber, seeded and finely diced
1 teaspoon wine vinegar
1 tablespoon chopped fresh herbs

Drain the salmon, then flake it and mix with the *fromage frais* (mayonnaise would be the non-dietary alternative). Mix the cucumber dice with the vinegar then drain and mix into the salmon. Spread on the toast slices and sprinkle with fresh herbs.

Instead of the cucumber, you could use fennel. A can of tuna could be used instead of the salmon, along with tiny dice of red pepper.

STEAK TARTARE TOAST TOPPING

Steak tartare is one of life's delights for me – and it can still remain so on my diet. The lean beef isn't too fattening, and the combined flavours are wonderful. For a special occasion, I would grill the bread black as usual, then cut out circles from the slices.

6 oz (175 g) lean beef fillet, minced
6 spring onions, finely chopped
1 dessertspoon Worcestershire sauce
½ teaspoon dry English mustard powder
salt and freshly ground black pepper
1 dessertspoon tomato ketchup
1 tablespoon small capers, drained
1 heaped tablespoon chopped fresh parsley

Mix all the ingredients together, except the capers and parsley, and spread over the toast. Top with the capers then sprinkle on the chopped parsley.

Sandwiches made with fresh wholemeal bread, little or no butter or marge, and meat, eggs, fish, cheese or salads, make well-balanced and nutritious meals.

BAKED POTATOES

The carbohydrate starch of potatoes may not seem to be very appropriate, but one very famous slimming book had a whole chapter on baked potatoes because of their fibre content (which is found in and near the skin). Potatoes actually have very little fat, no cholesterol at all, and several vitamins and minerals, notably potassium; one baked 4 oz (100 g) potato can supply 10 mg of Vitamin C, which is 30 per cent of the recommended daily allowance for an adult.

It's the toppings we use – butter, soured cream etc – that add on calories. Some of the ideas below won't be too damaging, and served with a salad, can make for a satisfying and healthy light meal.

PER PERSON

1 potato, at least 8 oz (225 g) in weight
1 tablespoon skimmed milk
1 oz (25 g) filling of choice (see below)
salt and freshly ground black pepper

Pre-heat the oven to gas mark 7, 425°F (220°C).

Scrub the potato clean, dry well then wrap in foil, dull side in. Bake in the pre-heated oven for 1¼ hours.

Remove, unwrap, then, as the potato starts cooling, cut off a 'lid' and scoop the lovely fluffy middle out into a bowl. Mash with the milk, then mix in the chosen filling and seasoning to taste.

Pile the mixture back into the potato skin. Most of the fillings can be served straightaway, but you can also return the potatoes to the oven for 10–15 minutes to serve hot rather than warm.

BAKED POTATO FILLINGS

1. Chopped celery, apple and skinned tomato with a little grated Cheddar cheese.

2. A little home-made tomato sauce (see p. 96) with some mashed canned sardine, tuna or salmon.

3. Left-over meat or poultry bits with lots of fresh herbs. You could add chutney or Worcestershire sauce for extra flavour.

4. Left-over fish flakes mixed with yoghurt and some anchovy essence.

5. Left-over diced vegetables with chutney or curry powder and a raw egg.

6. Chopped cooked spinach with Pesto Sauce (see p. 162).

7. Raw grated vegetables (radishes, courgettes, carrots, etc) with a little horseradish cream and lots of herbs.

8. Greek yoghurt or *fromage frais* with additional herbs, spices and other flavourings of choice. Serve these without reheating.

9. 1 × 225 g tin sugar-free baked beans (lovely served with a watercress salad).

SOUFFLÉ BAKED POTATOES

These are a little different from ordinary baked potatoes, but very light and tasty.

SERVES 4

4 potatoes, at least 8 oz (225 g) each in weight
salt and freshly ground black pepper
4 oz (100 g) cottage or curd cheese
1–2 tablespoons grated Parmesan cheese
2 teaspoons coarse-grain mustard
2 small eggs, separated

Pre-heat the oven and cook the potatoes as on p. 103. Unwrap and cool a little. Reduce the temperature of the oven to gas mark 5, 375°F (190°C).

Take a slice lengthwise off the top of each (rather than a small lid). Scoop the flesh of each out into a bowl, leaving a good 'shell'. Don't forget to scrape the flesh from the slice as well.

Mix seasoning to taste, the cottage or curd cheese, half the Parmesan, the mustard and egg yolks into the potato flesh. Whisk the egg whites until stiff and fold lightly into the mixture, and spoon back into the potato shells. Sprinkle with the remaining Parmesan and bake in the oven for a further 15–20 minutes until the potatoes puff up and turn golden. Eat immediately.

TUNA ROSTI

A wedge of this, along with a crisp green salad or tomato salad, makes a delicious lunch or supper dish.

SERVES 4–6

4 oz (100 g) onions, peeled and finely chopped
1 tablespoon sunflower oil
12 oz (350 g) potatoes, peeled, grated and dried
finely grated zest of 1 lemon
1 × 8 oz (225 g) can of tuna in brine, drained
salt and freshly ground black pepper
½ teaspoon freshly grated nutmeg

Using a 10 in (25 cm) non-stick frying-pan, fry the onion in the oil until just coloured. Remove onion with a slotted spoon, draining oil back into the pan. Mix the onion with all the other ingredients in a bowl. Return to the same pan and press down well to make a big potato cake.

Cook over a medium heat for 15 minutes then turn over (using a plate) and cook for a further 15 minutes. Serve hot.

Never sit around at the table after a meal – get up straightaway and do something else (preferably something more stimulating than the washing-up!).

BAKED LEEKS WITH TOMATOES

Breadcrumbs? You might well ask, but there aren't many and you need the texture and flavour they will give. Use the skins and seeds of the tomatoes and the herb stalks in the stock pot.

SERVES 4

1 lb (450 g) leeks (prepared weight)
1 tablespoon olive oil
a few dashes of Worcestershire sauce
2 tablespoons chopped fresh herbs (parsley with a little marjoram and oregano would be ideal)
4 beef tomatoes, skinned, halved and de-seeded
salt and freshly ground black pepper

Savoury breadcrumbs

4 oz (100 g) wholemeal bread, crusts removed
1 oz (25 g) hard cheese (Cheddar or Parmesan)
1 spring onion, trimmed
4 large sprigs fresh parsley
a pinch of dry English mustard powder

Pre-heat the oven to gas mark 5, 375°F (190°C).

Slice the leeks into ¼ in (5 mm) thick circles, then wash and separate into rings. Pat dry in a teatowel. In a 12 in (30 cm) frying-pan, heat the olive oil, then add the leek rings. Using a continuous, brisk stirring motion, stir-fry on a high heat for 6 minutes. Transfer to a shallow ovenproof dish, sprinkle with a few dashes of Worcestershire sauce and chopped herbs.

Arrange the tomatoes, cut edge down, on top of the leeks and season with salt and pepper. Cover with a lid or foil and bake in the oven for 30 minutes.

Meanwhile, make the Savoury Breadcrumbs. Simply whizz all the ingredients in a food processor.

Remove the leek and tomato dish from the oven and take off the lid. Liberally cover with the herbed breadcrumbs. Heat up the grill, and then crisp up the breadcrumb topping. Keep an eye on it so it doesn't burn, but do allow it to get crispy and browned.

BAKED STUFFED RED PEPPERS

These are delicious served with a fresh tomato herb sauce (see p. 96) and a crisp salad. They are very satisfying and have a wonderful flavour.

SERVES 4

4 red peppers, approx. 6 oz (175 g) each
1 tablespoon olive oil
12 oz (350 g) onions, peeled and finely chopped
1 lb (450 g) lean mutton, minced
salt and freshly ground black pepper
2 teaspoons curry paste or powder
8 tablespoons vegetable stock (see p. 86)
6 teaspoons grated Parmesan cheese
2 heaped tablespoons chopped fresh herbs
2 eggs, beaten

P re-heat the oven to gas mark 5, 375°F (190°C).

Wipe the peppers clean. Cut a thin slice off the end, as near the stalk as possible, and using a small sharp knife, remove the white pith and all the seeds from the insides.

In a non-stick frying pan heat the oil and then cook the onion until well browned. Add the minced meat, seasoning and curry paste. Stir-fry for 15 minutes, adding 4 tablespoons of the vegetable stock if the meat gets too dry. Leave to go cold.

Add the Parmesan, herbs and the eggs and mix thoroughly. Divide the meat mixture between the peppers, using a teaspoon.

Cut four double thicknesses of foil, big enough to completely wrap each pepper. Stand each filled pepper on foil, dull side in, then bring up the sides of foil. Put a tablespoon of stock into the base, then bring all the edges of foil together to make a closed packet. Put in an ovenproof dish or tray, small enough that they all support each other upright. Place in the pre-heated oven and bake for 1 hour, 20 minutes.

VEGETABLE LASAGNE

This is a wonderful alternative to a traditional lasagne, made with minced meat. The flavours are magnificent, and it's very healthy too! Ideal for a vegetarian lunch or supper.

SERVES 4 GENEROUSLY

1 tablespoon sunflower oil

6 oz (175 g) onions, peeled and diced

18 sheets no-need-to-cook lasagne, about 6 oz (175 g)

12 oz (350 g) courgettes, sliced in circles

1 medium aubergine, about 8 oz (225 g), thinly sliced

2 tablespoons sesame seeds, toasted

8 oz (225 g) tomatoes, skinned, de-seeded and sliced

2 tablespoons chopped fresh seasonal herbs

6 oz (175 g) medium white mushrooms, wiped, sliced, and soaked in the juice of 2 oranges

Custard and topping

10 fl oz (300 ml) *fromage frais*

2 egg yolks

salt, black pepper and nutmeg

3 oz (75 g) Jordan's crunchy oats

Pre-heat the oven to gas mark 4, 350°F (180°C). Grease a deepish ovenproof dish, 9 × 11 in (23 × 28 cm) with a little of the oil.

Gently fry the onion in the remaining oil until soft.

Arrange four sheets of lasagne on the base of the dish and top with the courgette circles, followed by the aubergine circles. (If the aubergine is older, it may need to be 'degorged' of its juices: simply sprinkle the slices with salt, leave in a colander, then rinse and dry.) Sprinkle the aubergine with the toasted sesame seeds.

Arrange another four lasagne sheets on top, then cover with the tomato slices, softened onions and herbs. Top with a further four lasagne sheets, then cover with the mushrooms and juice. Finally cover the whole top of the lasagne with the remaining six lasagne sheets.

For the topping mix together the *fromage frais*, egg yolks and seasoning to taste. Pour over the contents of the dish, then sprinkle with the crunchy oats. Bake in the pre-heated oven for 1 hour. Serve hot.

PORK CHOPS WITH ELDERFLOWER

We are most fortunate, here in the English Lakes, because a local person – Mr Woodall of Waberthwaite – has recently had the honour of the Royal Appointment bestowed on him for his pork. At the hotel we have been enjoying his produce for many years now, and when I started more 'serious eating', the prospect of giving up his lovely, thick, tasty, fatty chops was most distressing. However, I now cook them in the following way, although I do not eat a single scrap of the actual fat. Do use the elderflowers if you can, as they give the chops a lovely sweet, musty flavour. This, when you're on a diet, is tantamount to sin!

SERVES 4

4 thick chops, weighing approx. 8 oz (225 g) each
1½ pints (900 ml) water
2 tablespoons dried elderflowers, or 1 dessertspoon salt

In the bottom of your steamer, bring the water and elderflowers (or the salt) to the boil. Put the chops in the top of the steamer over the water, and put the lid on. Cook for 45 minutes.

Only you will know just how long your thick-bottomed, non-stick frying pan takes to get absolutely sizzling hot. When the pork chops have been steamed, you simply plunge them into the hot pan and, using a wooden spoon, press them down as hard as possible. They will sizzle and spit, and you will be amazed at the amount of fat that comes out. They look lovely and 'barbecued' after 2–3 minutes on each side, and taste succulent and tender when you eat them. Eat yours *minus* the fat, please!

AUBERGINE AND HERB LOAF

Aubergines are very low in calories (and contain quite a few nutritional goodies), but most people exclude them from diets because they think they can only cook them by frying. This recipe bakes the aubergine into a loaf that can be sliced and eaten alone as a lunch dish with a salad, or as the tasty base for grilled sliced tomatoes or a little scrambled egg.

SERVES 4–6

8 oz (225 g) aubergines

salt and freshly ground black pepper

vegetable oil for greasing

2 medium eggs

2 oz (50 g) stale wholemeal breadcrumbs

1½ oz (40 g) Parmesan cheese, grated

**2 tablespoons chopped fresh herbs
(basil, parsley, chives etc)**

2½ fl oz (75 ml) olive oil

2 fat juicy garlic cloves, peeled

1 tablespoon tomato purée

½ tablespoon Worcestershire sauce

2 oz (50 g) shelled nuts, finely chopped

Wipe the aubergines and cut in half lengthways. Place skin-side down on a rack over a tray. Sprinkle with salt and leave for 2–3 hours, to sweat out any sour juices.

Pre-heat the oven to gas mark 6, 400°F (200°C), and lightly grease a 1 lb (450 g) loaf tin with oil.

Place all the ingredients except the aubergine and nuts in a food processor and blend until smooth. Meanwhile, pat the aubergine halves dry on kitchen paper, and mince or chop fairly finely. Spread the nuts on a baking tray and toast in the pre-heating oven until they begin to turn brown.

Mix the aubergines and nuts into the egg mixture, and pour it into the prepared tin. Cook in the pre-heated oven for 15 minutes, then turn the oven down to gas mark 4, 350°F (180°C). Cook for a further 15 minutes. Test that the loaf is cooked by sliding a skewer into the middle – it should come out clean. If still slightly soggy, return it to the oven and cook for a further 5–10 minutes.

When cooked, remove the tin from the oven and leave for 10 minutes covered with foil or a teatowel. Turn out, slice and serve.

Dried pulses are a good slimming aid. They are high in bulk and fibre, so satisfy you for longer.

CHICK PEA SALAD WITH HOT BLACK ONIONS

Chick peas are very filling, so only eat this sparingly. The tastes are divine, though.

SERVES 6

12 oz (350 g) dried chick peas, soaked overnight in cold water

salt

4 oz (100 g) sultanas, soaked overnight in the juice of 1 lemon

1 Granny Smith apple

4 tablespoons chopped fresh parsley

Onions
2 tablespoons cooking oil
3 large onions, peeled and thinly sliced into circles

Curry vinaigrette
5 fl oz (150 ml) French dressing
4 teaspoons Curry Essence (see p. 88)

Drain the chick peas, checking for stones, then rinse thoroughly. Place in a saucepan, cover with cold water, and bring to the boil. Simmer for approximately 1½ hours until soft. About 20 minutes before they are cooked, add 1 level teaspoon salt. Drain well. While the chick peas are still piping hot, place them in a large mixing bowl.

Mix the vinaigrette ingredients together well and pour over the chick peas, adding the sultanas and their lemon juice, and mix well. Stir occasionally while cooling and when cold, cover and remove to the fridge.

About 2 hours prior to serving, remove from the fridge and decant into a serving dish. Quarter the apple (do not peel it) and remove the core. Slice each quarter into four and cut into small dice. Add the apple dice and 3 tablespoons of the chopped parsley. Mix well.

Half an hour prior to serving heat the oil and fry the onions, stirring frequently over a medium heat, until quite literally they are black. This will take about 30 minutes. Have the extractor fan on, or the window open!

Tip the hot onions over the chick pea salad and sprinkle on remaining chopped parsley and serve.

CUMBERLAND SAUSAGE AND SPICED LENTIL HOT POT

When on a diet for some time there are the odd occasions when you really feel you want a bloody good blow-out. That's when I go for this recipe: it's very comforting. The endless tubes of Cumberland sausage often contain a lot of fat, but having found a good supplier do try this recipe. All the fat is initially cooked out and you are left with the lightly spiced meat as the filler.

SERVES 6 AT LEAST

1½ lb (700 g) length of Cumberland sausage (or you can use spicy Italian or Spanish if you prefer)

Spiced lentils

12 oz (350 g) onions, peeled and diced
2 tablespoons vegetable oil
seeds from 6 cardamom pods
2 teaspoons freshly ground coriander seeds
2 teaspoons turmeric
12 oz (350 g) split orange lentils
2½ pints (1.5 litres) chicken or vegetable stock (see p. 86)
salt and freshly ground black pepper
1 × 8 oz (225 g) Bramley cooking apple

Pre-heat the oven to gas mark 5, 375°F (190°C). Place the lengthy twirl of sausage on a wire rack over a baking tray and bake for 45 minutes, turning half-way through the cooking time. You will be amazed at how much fat comes out of the sausage! The skin should be quite brown, and fairly dry. Leave to cool.

For the lentils, use a large flameproof casserole. On the top of your stove sweat the onions in the oil until soft, then add the spices. Stir well, then add the lentils, stock, salt and pepper. Cook over a very low heat for 30 minutes with the lid on.

Peel and core the apple and cut into large dice. Cut the sausage into ½ inch (1 cm) lengths. Add both to the casserole, stir in and cook for a further 20 minutes.

117

The dish can be prepared in advance. Leave everything to cool, then refrigerate overnight. When you wish to serve, pre-heat the oven to the same temperature as above, then warm the casserole through for 20 minutes.

SAVOURY LENTILS

When I was a child, split peas, butter beans, etc played a large part in family fare because they were relatively inexpensive. When I flitted the family nest and started earning money myself, I went off them. Now they are very much back in favour . . . well, lentils are. They make a satisfying meal when you are dieting – but don't eat too many . . .!

Cook according to the packet instructions (they do vary so), but 10 minutes before they are supposed to be ready, remove from the stove. Strain, but measure how much water is left. Dry the lentils for a minute and then put back in the equivalent amount of stock (see p. 86), and finish off the cooking.

For each 4 oz (100 g) of lentils cooked, throw in 2 peeled and coarsely chopped tomatoes, or sufficient Curry Essence (see p. 88) to provide the flavouring that satisfies *you*. I think you'll notice the difference!

PRAWNS AND BROWN RICE

The carbohydrate, fibre and nutrients of brown rice are useful in any diet. This slightly eastern combination makes a delightful main course for a lunch or supper – slimmers just shouldn't eat too much of it! A salad would be an ideal accompaniment, and you could, if you liked, offer a dollop of home-made tomato sauce (see p. 96).

SERVES 4

2 tablespoons sesame oil
1 large onion, about 8 oz (225 g), peeled and finely diced
2 large garlic cloves, peeled and made into a paste with 1 teaspoon salt
salt and freshly ground black pepper
juice and finely grated zest of 1 lime
14 oz (400 g) brown rice
1¼ pints (750 ml) boiling vegetable stock or water
1 lb (450 g) shelled prawns, defrosted and well dried
8 oz (225 g) frozen peas, defrosted
3 oz (75 g) flaked almonds, toasted
1 heaped tablespoon roughly chopped fresh coriander

In a large lidded pan, heat the oil then add the diced onion and crushed garlic. Cook gently until the onion is soft and just colouring. Add black pepper, lime zest and juice and the rice. Stir to mix. Pour on the boiling liquid and bring back to the boil. Cover with a well fitting lid, reduce to a low heat, and cook for 40–45 minutes.

Turn up the heat, remove the lid, and add the prawns, peas and two-thirds of the almonds. Mix well, check seasoning, and stir for 3–4 minutes until all is heated through. Transfer to a serving dish and top with the remaining nuts and the fresh coriander. Serve immediately.

MARINATED SPICED FISH

This is a dish I always keep in individual portions in my freezer as I can then have one pack when I'm alone at the farm, or serve several as a main course with a lightly dressed green salad for a supper party. This is not one of the prettiest dishes, but the combination of flavours and the meaty texture of the fish always make me feel as if I've had a suitably filling feast!

With more years behind me and less ahead, I seem to be becoming a creature of habit, and find myself repeating certain things at certain times of the year. The one constant in my diary is my winter visit to Cape Town where I stay in a splendid small hotel called Greenways which, in many ways, is similar to Miller Howe. There are thirteen rooms, a beautifully kept large garden, a large swimming pool and a delightful dog-in-residence called Matthew, whom I take for daily walks on the mountains at the crack of dawn. It's a house with a heart as big as that of its manageress, Jean Macdonald.

Whatever day of the week I arrive, I always have my first lunch with my closest friends, Judge Wilfrid Cooper

*and his lovely wife Gertrude, who gave me this recipe.
Each year Gertrude (on the last of our weekly telephone
calls closest to my arrival) asks, 'What would you like for
lunch, John?' I always choose mealies (corn-on-the-cob)
straight from her garden, followed by 'Your spiced fish!'
Some folks may think this attitude boring but now, as I
approach sixty, I find there is something secure and
loving about such a routine.*

SERVES 6

**2 lb (900 g) white fish fillets (cod, halibut or sole), cut into
neat, even pieces**

3 tablespoons plain flour

1 level teaspoon cornflour

salt and freshly ground black pepper

vegetable oil

Marinade

8 oz (225 g) onions, peeled and sliced into rings

4 tablespoons olive oil

2 level tablespoons curry powder or essence (see p. 88)

5 fl oz (150 ml) malt vinegar

1 level tablespoon soft brown sugar

1 heaped teaspoon turmeric

Dredge the pieces of fish with the plain flour and
cornflour, then shake off the surplus. Season with
salt and pepper. Fry eight pieces at a time in a
tablespoon of oil, browning lightly on each side.
Drain on absorbent paper and leave to cool. Fry the
remainder of the fish in the same way, and if the

frying pan looks tacky at any stage, wipe it clean with kitchen paper. Use a tablespoon of oil for each new batch.

For the marinade, cook the onion rings in the oil until soft and golden. In a saucepan mix the remaining ingredients together to a smooth texture and then add the cooked onions. Simmer gently for 5 minutes then set aside to cool.

Pack the cold fried fish into a plastic container and cover with the cold marinade. Cover and refrigerate for 4–5 days, turning daily. Serve cold with a green salad.

APPLE AND APRICOT CRUMBLE

Most crumble toppings use more butter and sugar than this. But think of how little of the actual topping you will have when it's divided out between the four of you. Serve with crème fraîche, fromage frais or Greek yoghurt instead of cream.

SERVES 4

12 oz (350 g) Bramley cooking apples, peeled, cored and sliced
4 oz (100 g) dried apricots, soaked in water overnight
1 teaspoon grated lemon zest
2 oz (50 g) soft brown sugar

Crumble topping
4 oz (100 g) wholemeal flour
½ oz (15 g) rolled oats
2 oz (50 g) unsalted butter
1 oz (25 g) soft brown sugar

Pre-heat the oven to gas mark 4, 350°F (180°C).

Combine the raw apple slices, apricots, zest and sugar and place in the base of a 2 pint (1.1 litre) baking dish. Mix the crumble topping ingredients together and sprinkle over the fruit evenly. Bake in the pre-heated oven for 45–60 minutes.

If you are too fat, you are more likely to get diabetes in middle age. You are also more likely to suffer from arthritis and high blood pressure.

CARROT AND NUT CAKE

Before I started my binge diet, I was a devil for desserts. Quite apart from 'quality controlling' all the six puddings on the dinner menu, if, at the end of the night, there were any left over, one and often two would always find their way to my place at the staff supper table.

This carrot and nut cake is one I found hard to give up, so I adjusted it and used low-fat cream cheese instead of the usual vast amount of butter. It isn't as light and feathery as my old one, but oh, it does make you feel as if you are having a good old-fashioned pud once more.

SERVES 8

2 oz (50 g) soft butter

4 oz (100 g) soft brown sugar

1 lb (450 g) carrots, peeled and coarsely grated

4 oz (100 g) low-fat cream cheese

4 oz (100 g) shelled pecan nuts, coarsely chopped

1 level teaspoon freshly grated nutmeg

1 free-range egg, lightly beaten

4 oz (100 g) sultanas, soaked overnight in 2 tablespoons brandy

8 oz (225 g) self-raising flour, sieved

3 egg whites

Topping and filling

10 fl oz (300 ml) *fromage frais*

2 tablespoons home-made or good bought lemon curd

124

Pre-heat the oven to gas mark 4, 350°F (180°C) and line the base and sides of a 9 inch (23 cm) spring-clip cake tin with good quality greaseproof paper.

Melt the butter in a saucepan, then beat in the sugar. Wait until it becomes syrupy, then stir in the prepared carrots and simmer for 5 minutes. Allow to cool, then turn into a mixing bowl. Beat in the soft cheese, then fold in the nuts, nutmeg and egg along with the brandied sultanas. Fold in the sieved flour. Beat the egg whites until stiff and fold these into the mix.

Pour into the prepared tin and bake for 45 minutes. Cool in the tin. When cold, split in two. Mix the topping and filling ingredients together. Use half to sandwich the cake halves together, then spread the other half on the top. Mark the top with a fork to give a pattern.

About 4 oz (100 g) of cooked carrot supplies over 20,000 times the recommended daily allowance of Vitamin A for a healthy adult. (Vitamin A is not lost in cooking.)

BAKED RUM BANANAS

Bananas aren't the most slimming of fruits, but when cooked they have such an intense flavour that a little goes a long way.

SERVES 4

4 large bananas
6 fl oz (175 ml) dark rum
about 9 oz (250 g) *crème fraîche* or Greek yoghurt
1 oz (25 g) each of sesame seeds and sunflower seeds, toasted

Pre-heat oven to gas mark 4, 350°F (180°C).

Peel the bananas and slice them through into ½ in (1 cm) lengths. Place in an ovenproof dish with a lid, pour on the rum and bake in the pre-heated oven for about 30 minutes. The bananas should have gone soft, but not totally mushy. Stir to coat them in any rum that is remaining.

Divide banana and rum between four heatproof bowls or glasses. Top with a large dollop of yoghurt or *crème fraîche* and sprinkle with toasted seeds. Eat immediately.

FRUITY *CREME FRAICHE* PUDDING

This is simplicity itself, and any seasonal fruit can be substituted for the grapes – fresh raspberries, wedges of nectarine or peach, strawberries or segments of clementine. If you happen to leave the mixture overnight, it becomes thick and muesli-like – ideal for a delicious breakfast treat!

SERVES 4

9 oz (250 g) *crème fraîche*
2 oz (50 g) dried dates (or fresh, stoned), chopped
8 oz (225 g) grapes, seeded and halved
4 oz (100 g) Jordan's crunchy oats
2 oz (50 g) toasted sunflower seeds or toasted chopped hazelnuts

Mix everything together well, except the seeds or nuts. Divide between four serving glasses. Top with the toasted seeds or nuts.

Don't pick at children's unfinished plates, or stick your finger into cake mixing bowls etc. Wash plates and bowls immediately to remove temptation. It's better to waste food than add to your waist.

COMPOTE OF DRIED FRUIT

Dried fruits are full of nutritional benefits, and taste delicious whether cooked as here or simply nibbled as a snack. Serve the compote with some natural yoghurt if you like and sprinkle that *with the toasted nuts.*

SERVES 4

3 oz (75 g) each of dried apricots, dried apple rings, dried peaches and prunes (or any selection of choice)
1 oz (25 g) large seedless raisins
1 orange
½ cinnamon stick
2 oz (50 g) flaked almonds, briefly toasted

Rinse the dried fruit, then soak in cold water to cover for several hours or overnight.

Add the raisins, juice of the orange and the cinnamon to the soaking fruit and transfer to a pan. Cut the rind of the orange into large pieces and add. Simmer gently for about 20 minutes, making sure there is still some liquid left, or until soft. Leave to cool.

To serve, remove the orange rind and cinnamon. Sprinkle at the last minute with the toasted almonds.

Always try to eat the skins of fruit such as apples, pears, peaches and nectarines as they contain fibre.

128

FRUIT SALAD

This must be the best possible dessert for the slimmer – or anyone else for that matter. At any time of year there is always some fruit that can be included. Once I might have used rum, a wine or a wonderful liqueur to macerate the fruits, but orange or apple juice is much less damaging to the waistline!

For maximum effect for a dinner party, say, present the fruit salad in a fruit container – a scooped-out watermelon to serve everyone, or a small Gallia or other melon for individual servings. (Use the flesh in the fruit salad, of course.)

Serve with some fromage frais, crème fraîche *or natural yoghurt if you like.*

SERVES 4

**2 lb (1 kg) assorted fruits
juice of 1 lemon
10 fl oz (300 ml) orange juice
50 g (2 oz) shelled nuts, toasted and chopped**

Prepare the fruit as appropriate, peeling, stoning, cutting, slicing. The following are a few suggestions: apple chunks or balls; diagonal banana slices; carambola or star fruit slices; stoned cherries; seeded grapes; kiwifruit slices; mango chunks; melon chunks or balls; orange segments; peach or nectarine slices; fresh pineapple chunks; raspberries and strawberries. A few, like the apple and banana, should be tossed in the lemon juice to prevent discoloration.

Mix together in a large bowl with the orange juice. Chill for an hour or so. Just before serving, sprinkle with the chopped nuts.

Vegetable and Fruit Juices

If I have been away on holiday or working, it goes without saying that a couple of extra pounds are invariably added to my frame. Thus, when I get back to the farm, I religiously have a 24-hour period when I only eat fruit and drink raw juices. It is what I call my Day of Detoxification! At first this was orange or grapefruit juice, but then some kind friends bought me a juice extractor which is regularly used these days. I must admit it is a chore to dismantle, wash clean and dry, but well worth the effort. In fact I quite often serve chilled fruit or vegetable juices as a starter instead of a cooked soup.

You could actually serve these juices as healthy, non-alcoholic fruit and vegetable 'cocktails'. However, the canapés have to be simply radishes or wedges of chilled celery. No fancy puff pastry cases filled with rich pâté or handfuls of crisps and nuts!

I have recently discovered that vegetable and fruit juices are the basis of one of the most famous and successful remedies for fatigue, stress and ageing in spas around the world – the *Rohsäft Kur* (raw juice cure). The process involved is not completely understood, but the juices put the entire body through a kind of spring cleaning. No wonder I feel so well after even a day!

Juices work out quite expensive as you'll need about 4–5 lb (1.8–2.25 kg) of raw celery, say, to make 2 pints (1.2 litres) juice, but they are *so* good for you, abounding in vitamins, minerals and other nutrients. Initially I opted for straightforward carrot juice for its Vitamin A content, as I had been told that 8 oz (225 g) juiced carrot only produced about 50 calories. It was, however, a midwife who told me to drink half carrot juice and half skimmed milk to get additional benefit from this easily obtained, all-year-round vegetable. Now I mix and combine as readily as any medieval alchemist, using my extractor rather like a vegetable stockpot as I literally throw in anything that takes my fancy. The end result sometimes may not always be high in deliciousness, but this is soon rectified by the addition of lots of fresh garden herbs.

My grandmother used to dabble with herbs and was forever, according to my father, wasting her time and money at the local herbalist's shop in Barrow's Dalton Road. She certainly was not a hypochondriac, but I vividly remember that each and every Saturday she would spend a great deal of time in this fascinat-

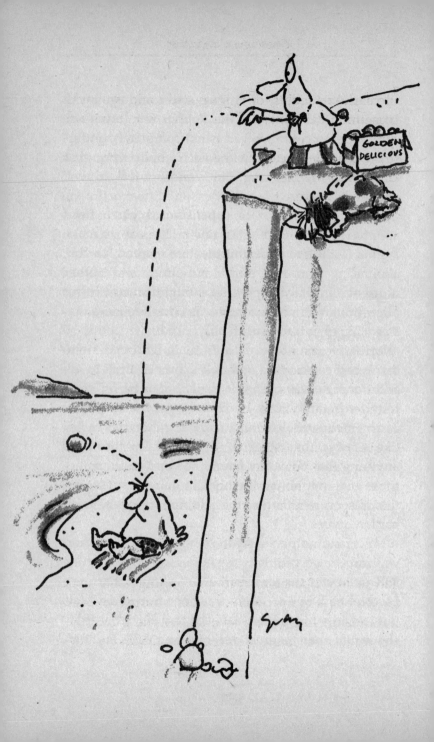

ing dark and slightly dirty shop, and come away with something different that was supposed to transform her life.

Brought up during World War Two, I clearly recall constantly being told that although food was rationed, we were the healthiest and fittest nation on earth. On reflection, I can't help but think that this was official propaganda as, when I was at school, it was as common as a winter cold to have acne and boils all year round! My friends' acne was helped along with a horrible greasy commercial cream and lots of over-cooked spinach. Their boils were poulticed and then bound with mag. sulph.

My afflictions were treated at home by the old-fashioned methods. Whenever I was ill herb medicines were always used, as, apart from being much cheaper than a visit to the doctor, they were always on hand on the second to top shelf of the corner cupboard in the living room. My grandmother lived a remarkably busy life, having to work most of it in order to keep the family together and, on reflection, she was a very fit and active lady right up to the end.

APPLE

Please do support our rapidly expanding home apple producers who are valiantly endeavouring to bring back many old favourite strains. The one apple that I never, ever use is the French Golden Delicious. They are neither golden nor delicious, and when I retire I think I will spend time on the White Cliffs of Dover lobbing every ruddy one back across the Channel!

Apples are high in Vitamin C, and are excellent for purifying the blood and cleansing the skin; my grandmother used to swear by 2 teaspoons of cider vinegar in a glass of warm water each morning to retain her girlish complexion!

As far as juice is concerned, it's good (try combining with carrot), but it's better to eat them whole: that way they keep blood sugar levels up, making you feel fuller for longer – a considerable bonus for the dieter.

APRICOT

This is a fruit that seems never, these days, to taste as it did years ago. Apricots have a relatively short season: look for mature, well-coloured tender fruits with no sign of shrivelling, and use more or less on the day of purchase. They are a good source of Vitamin A – 4 oz (100 g) contain one-third of the recommended daily allowance for adults.

BEETROOT

This much-maligned vegetable played a great part in my early childhood as we used to have it in all forms – pickled, boiled, roasted and stir-fried. In Germany the juice is sold pasteurised as it is believed to be an excellent pick-you-up for invalids (particularly good for the blood). When I make pure beetroot juice, which is *strong*, I find it much enhanced with fresh mint and a little cider vinegar. You could also mix it with carrot juice.

BRUSSELS SPROUTS

A favourite of mine, but did you know when served raw (they can be grated into a winter salad) or as juice they will give you, weight for weight, twice the amount of Vitamin C as an orange? Try improving the taste by mixing with a little orange juice.

CABBAGE

Many folk can't stand this lovely vegetable and, in the North particularly, it used to be put on to cook as soon as breakfast was over and served up disgustingly tasteless, but smelly, and limp for lunch. It's good as a juice though, and I also use the stalk in my juice extractor. Spring and summer cabbages are best, they're more juicy. Try mixing with carrot juice.

Try not to go shopping on an empty stomach – you'll buy much more than you need (*and* eat it).

135

CARROT

This is the most familiar vegetable juice – good for the digestion and for the skin. It contains a large amount of Vitamin A (so don't drink *too* much), and use it to improve the flavours of many other juices. 1 lb (450 g) clean carrots will give you a delicious, sweet 10 fl oz (300 ml) juice, but if you want to add a little oomph to it, also juice 1 oz (25 g) onion. (I often double this!)

CELERY

I have always liked celery and eat it quite a lot, so I find it disturbing when told by the experts that it is the finest thing to help arthritis. I am riddled with this and even though I invariably put a stick of celery into most of my vegetable juices, it hasn't helped me one bit.

In the States, celery juice is used as an anti-ulcer remedy, and at a health farm in the Cape I was served pure celery juice lukewarm, sweetened with a little locally produced honey as a cocktail before supper – it was supposed to reduce our desire for food.

For a 'coleslaw' type dish, try coating grated carrots, cucumber etc with natural yoghurt.

CUCUMBER

This is extremely easy to juice in the machine. I know a beautician who never eats the skin but stores it in a plastic bag in the fridge and twice a day she wipes her hands with it. I must admit that her hands – and she's now in her late sixties – are beautifully smooth, but why, oh why, I ask myself, did she never use it on her face?!

Cucumber is extremely low in calories so is good for your diet, and for flushing out the system (it's a diuretic). Try blending it with carrot or beetroot. An English cucumber weighing approximately 1 lb (450 g) when juiced produces 10 fl oz (300 ml) thin, tasty juice. If you add the juice of 8 oz (225 g) celery, you will be amazed at the difference.

DANDELION

Each spring as kids we were dosed with dandelion and wild spring nettle juice to purge us of any winter ills. Close to the farm there is a traditional old-fashioned herbalist's shop which is nearly always full of locals taking their home-made dandelion and burdock drink – hot in the winter and cold in the summer.

The leaves are high in iron and Vitamins C and E, but only use in the spring as I find them very bitter towards the end of summer.

137

GARLIC

This is one of the cure-alls of herbal medicine, and it was used during the World Wars against septic poisoning, gangrene, typhus and dysentery for its antibiotic properties. My machine won't cope with garlic on its own – a juice would be fairly ghastly – but I often add a couple of cloves to other juices, for that medicinal property, and for flavour.

GREEN BEAN

The juice of French beans particularly is said to be good for sufferers of gout when mixed with the juice of Brussels sprouts.

LEMON AND LIME

I use a lot of lemons and limes in cooking as the flavours are so distinct. They are full of Vitamin C, and as they have little sodium they are good for folk on a salt-free diet. Juice in a press rather than the extractor, and add to other juices, or have in a mug of hot water first thing in the morning as a tonic. Keeps scurvy at bay!

LETTUCE

A delicate salad plant, available in all sorts, sizes and shapes. I find the outer leaves (provided they aren't shrivelled or brown) as well as the base roots, add a hint of extra flavour to a juice. Most green leaves are high in iron, and lettuce is well known as a natural tranquilliser (useful to the stressed dieter).

NETTLE

Even these days I collect young spring nettles and if I don't use them in a nettle, barley and egg pudding to go with roast mutton, I add them to my juicer. They're rich in iron and Vitamin C – and are said to be good in treating arthritis.

ORANGE

I simply do these on my little circular juice extractor, and the juice is used daily at Miller Howe to make the morning's Buck's Fizz.

PARSLEY

Although a herb, this abounds with Vitamin C and has a high iron count. I adore both the flat and curly types. Use a little of the juice mixed with other juices such as carrot or celery.

PUMPKIN

The pumpkin season is relatively short and I, personally, do not like it juiced, but am always to be found nibbling toasted pumpkin seeds. These are excellent, too, on salads.

SPINACH

Each year my day is made when Mrs Wild from Winster comes in with her first offering of home-grown spinach. As a juice it's extremely good for you, helping the digestive system particularly. Combine it with other juices, and I find nutmeg or orange rind enhances it immensely.

TOMATO

Once again Mrs Wild's first crop of greenhouse-grown tomatoes sends me wild. I make them into simple salads with basil, into soups with red peppers and possibly redcurrants, and into juice. (My father would never touch tomatoes as he was quite positive the pips were the cause of his appendicitis; I've just read that, in a large study in Wales, tomatoes ranked high as a *protection* against appendicitis!) 1 lb (450 g) tomatoes will produce 10 fl oz (300 ml) fresh juice which only needs a little seasoning or a dash of Worcestershire sauce.

WATERCRESS

High in sulphur and iodine, the juice is valuable, but it shouldn't be drunk pure. I find it delicious mixed with celery and tomato or carrot and spinach. Half a bunch of watercress (about 2 oz/50 g) with 3 celery sticks (about 10 oz/275 g), 4 oz (100 g) radishes and about 6 oz (175 g) tomatoes (stalks and all) will give you 15 fl oz (450 ml) of 'cocktail'. To sweeten this, you can also add 4 oz (100 g) of either apple or pear, juiced; this produces 5 fl oz (150 ml).

To any or all of your juices, add a handful of fresh herbs, some seasoning if you like (go easy on the salt), or a little lemon juice. Pour from the extractor into a jug containing ice cubes (to reduce oxidation) and drink straightaway, or keep in the fridge for no longer than a few hours.

You will be surprised as to just how much *gunge* all these juiced items produce in the container of the juicer. Don't throw *any* of it away as it is so useful in the stock pot (see p. 86). If you don't want to use it straightaway, it can be frozen.

Instead of hot chocolate milk drinks, try Bovril. Alternatively spice a strong vegetable stock with some Worcestershire sauce and a tiny drop of Tabasco.

CHAPTER 3

ENTERTAINING
AT
HOME

When you entertain at home, you could easily prepare a *normal* dinner, shall we say, for your guests,
while you stick to a salad. However, this inevitably
becomes not only the talking point of the evening –
'Ooh, aren't you noble!', 'Being the martyr, are we?',
or, even worse, 'Off your marbles, dear' – but can
also make your guests feel a little uncomfortable.
This would not happen if you were eating out at a
restaurant – where you can all go your own way, so to
speak, choosing your own menu – and it can be a bit
of a problem. You want to give your friends the best,
but you also want to keep to your own dieting rules.

The answer is to cook delicious things which *do* fall
into your new eating plan. In the following pages I
have compiled six three-course dinner-party menus
which I bet my bottom dollar your guests will enjoy
and not even guess, for one moment, that they are
having diet food! You can, as usual, serve yourself slightly less than your companions, and if you
keep on pouring the wine as any good host or
hostess should, no-one will notice any of your
abstemiousness in either food or drink.

Starters

The starters in the six proposed menus are different,
delicious and, on the whole, dietary, but there are a
number of other things you could offer. Lightly

cooked traditional vegetable starters like artichokes or asparagus are a possibility, as long as you serve them with the merest touch of a French dressing or citrus juice instead of those lashings of melted butter. A small helping of ratatouille (made with a little oil, not butter) and some good bread would be tempting; or a wedge of melon with lots of ground ginger or a little Parma ham. Alternate slices of fresh pear and avocado pear arranged on the plate with a little dressing is good – as is an interesting salad.

Accompaniments

Once you are off the 'ever-so-bad-for-you' foods, you will, I feel sure, be very much aware that your taste-buds are much more alert and receptive. Having been involved in food for more years than I care to recall, I always pride myself on being able, when putting something into my mouth, to pick out nearly all the ingredients with ease. I must admit that for a while it became more tricky, but my tastebuds are now back on form!

I have always, but always, made a thing of vegetables whether serving dinner at the hotel, or a simple supper at the farm. Now I find that I cook most vegetables in *stock* rather than water. You will be amazed at how much more flavoursome they are.

However, there are many vegetables that can be

steamed or boiled, flavoured in different, non-fattening ways, and which do not cry out for a christening of butter. Try broad beans, green beans, or Brussels sprouts with just a touch of walnut oil and lots of black pepper; broccoli or cauliflower topped with toasted almonds; cabbage, chicory or courgettes cooked in orange juice; carrots glazed with citrus juice and sprinkled with ground caraway or coriander seeds or chopped herbs; celeriac cubes with lemon juice and thyme; quarters of fennel baked in foil with natural yoghurt; mange-touts with a little soy sauce; baked herby mushrooms; milk-baked baby onions; fresh garden peas with mint; or baked tomatoes. A small baked potato would not be too damaging either (see p. 103).

These days I tend to do a whopping great bowl of salad (see p. 77), and new potatoes, steamed and then tossed in heavily herbed low-fat natural yoghurt. (The potatoes look shiny, so folk think they are fattening!) This is usually sufficient, so I rarely bother with the numerous veg I used to love cooking and serving.

If you're hungry, nibble on healthy things like a large peeled mushroom, sprinkled with a little soy sauce, toasted sunflower seeds, cherry tomatoes, or cherries.

Desserts and Cheese

I once was the original chocoholic, and as for double or Jersey cream, I used it liberally with all my puds. I am equally generous now with yoghurt (the low-fat kind or Greek, depending on how sinful or otherwise I want to be), *fromage frais* or *crème fraîche*. All taste so good that no-one will really notice they're being denied the calories of cream. I occasionally sweeten them with a little local runny honey.

As for the cheese – before or after the dessert, as you like – I always bring out a large, beautiful old cheese dish and arrange on it some paper vine leaves and two or three local farm cheeses. (My cheeseboard often includes the Dolcelatte Torte which, as most of my friends know, is a passion of mine, and has to be part of my last supper.) Alongside the cheese dish I will offer a bowl of fresh radishes and a jar of good celery, or some polished apples and seedless grapes, along with some good home-made wholemeal bread.

I then sit back and watch the guests doing what I used to do. They just cannot leave the ruddy cheese-board alone. They go on taking just a little nick of that, and a large bit of that, and of course wanting another slice of the lovely brown bread. I slowly and carefully quarter my apple, remove the core and then little by little slice a piece off and devour it. Nobody is aware, nor do they take the slightest notice, of the fact that I am not being daft like them and shovelling

down the calories. (But, yes, I do occasionally have a teaspoon of the Dolcelatte to remind me of my wicked past!)

Menu One

MARINATED MUSHROOMS

A slice of good crusty bread is delicious with this for lunch, or for a dinner party starter, to mop up any juices. You could also serve the mushrooms in small ramekins.

SERVES 4

8 oz (225 g) white button mushrooms, wiped and thinly sliced
2 fl oz (50 ml) soya sauce
3 fl oz (85 ml) medium sherry
about 8 lettuce leaves

Simply marinate the mushroom slices in the soya sauce and sherry for 4 hours, or overnight, then serve, roughly drained, on a bed of the lettuce leaves.

Try chewing unsweetened gum if you need that stimulation. It helped me for a while – it keeps the jaws busy.

SALMON FISH CAKES

For those not worrying about calories, these fish cakes could be fried in a mixture of butter or oil. They could also be coated in the Savoury Breadcrumbs on p. 107.

MAKES 8 SMALL FISH CAKES

12 oz (350 g) lightly cooked salmon, boned
2 oz (50 g) fennel bulb, finely chopped
2 tablespoons fresh dill, coarsely chopped
8 oz (225 g) potatoes, peeled, boiled and mashed
salt and freshly ground black pepper
2 eggs
3 oz (75 g) fine fresh breadcrumbs
1 tablespoon chopped fresh parsley

Flake the salmon into a bowl, then add the fennel and dill. Mix well. Divide into eight portions.

Season the potato, then mix in the yolk of one of the eggs. Divide into eight portions, and mix each with a portion of fish. Flatten into circles. (You may need some flour to prevent stickiness.)

Mix the remaining egg whites and yolk together on a plate, and put the breadcrumbs and parsley mixed together on another. Dip each cake into the egg then in the breadcrumbs, then place on a baking tray, cover and chill.

When you want to cook, pre-heat the grill. Grill until golden on each side, about 10–15 minutes altogether.

TIRAMISU

The name of this Venetian pudding comes from the local dialect for 'pick-me-up' – referring undoubtedly to the alcohol content! (You could use whisky or rum instead of the brandy.) It is usually made with Mascarpone, a full-fat cow's milk cream cheese, or double cream. This version is much lighter.

SERVES 4–6

2 eggs, separated

3 oz (75 g) caster sugar

1 lb (450 g) low-fat soft cheese

5 fl oz (150 ml) natural yoghurt

5 fl oz (150 ml) cooking brandy

5 fl oz (150 ml) strong coffee (made with 3 heaped teaspoons good instant coffee)

6 oz (175 g) Boudoir sponge finger biscuits

3 teaspoons good cocoa powder

a chocolate flake or flakes of block chocolate to decorate (optional)

In a bowl, beat the egg yolks with the sugar until white and fluffy. Add the soft cheese, yoghurt and 2 tablespoons of the brandy, and beat until smooth. Whisk the egg whites until the same consistency, then fold into the creamy cheese mix.

Mix the coffee and the remaining brandy together. Separate the sponge finger biscuits into four equal piles. One by one, dip each finger from one of the piles in the coffee liquid and arrange in a layer to cover the base of an appropriate flattish serving dish. Cover with a third of the cream cheese mix and dust with a little of the sieved cocoa. Repeat this layering twice more, then finish with a final layer of coffee-soaked biscuits, a final dusting of cocoa and the flaked chocolate (if used). Chill for at least a few hours.

Menu Two

STUFFED APPLES

This starter is composed of a raw apple and various healthy ingredients in the stuffing. The principal advantage is that it is filling without being high in calories.

SERVES 4

4 medium Cox's apples
finely grated zest and juice of 1 lemon
1 oz (25 g) sultanas
6 oz (175 g) low-fat soft cheese
2 oz (50 g) seedless grapes, halved
2 oz (50 g) dried dates, chopped

Wipe the apples, then take a slice off the stalk end, like a little hat. Using a parisian scoop, remove the cores and discard. Scoop out a little more of the flesh in each apple to make a larger hole: keep the flesh and chop it (you'll need about 2 tablespoons in all). Brush the insides of the apple with some of the lemon juice; use the rest to prevent the chopped apple flesh browning and to plump the sultanas up (in the same bowl).

Mix together the soft cheese, grape halves, chopped dates, sultanas, apple flesh and lemon zest. Stuff into the holes in the apples, and put the lids back on. Serve immediately.

LOIN OF VENISON WITH RASPBERRY PURÉE

Venison is a very healthy meat because what fat there is lies around the meat and can easily be cut off, not marbled through it as with beef or lamb. This means, of course, that it can be very dry, but careful cooking should avoid this.

SERVES 4

12 oz (350 g) loin of venison, trimmed
4 garlic cloves, peeled and crushed
5 tablespoons olive oil
8 juniper berries, finely crushed

Raspberry purée

4 oz (100 g) raspberries
1 teaspoon icing sugar

Put the crushed garlic and 3 tablespoons of the olive oil into a shallow container that can be sealed. Add the trimmed loin to this marinade, seal and place in the fridge for 24 hours. Turn the meat at least twice during this time.

When you are ready to cook, pre-heat the oven to gas mark 8, 450°F (230°C).

Remove the loin from the marinade and pat dry. Put the marinade and the remaining olive oil into a small frying pan – one that can be transferred to your oven, so watch the handle. Bring the oil to the smoking stage then add the crushed juniper berries and blacken them. Add the loin to the hot oil, pressing down with a wooden spoon to seal sides and ends. This takes 2–3 minutes. Immediately put the pan into the pre-heated oven and roast for 15–20 minutes.

Make the raspberry purée by rubbing berries and sugar through a fine plastic sieve. Warm through or leave cold.

Let the venison rest for a minute or two, then carve and serve with the hot or cold fruit purée.

FRUIT YOGHURT ICE

Ice cream is one of the things that we feel we can't have when on a diet – but made with yoghurt instead of double cream, it can be an occasional, and not too damaging, treat. A nice end to a dinner party: your non-dieting friends could have a biscuit or two to accompany it.

SERVES 4

10 fl oz (300 ml) Greek yoghurt

4 tablespoons puréed summer fruits (strawberries, raspberries, currants, blackberries, loganberries etc)

1 tablespoon icing sugar

2 egg whites

Mix the yoghurt and fruit purée together with the sugar. (If the fruit has pips – like raspberries – sieve after liquidising.) Beat the egg whites until stiff, and fold into the yoghurt/fruit mixture. Pour into ramekins and freeze for at least 3 hours.

Soften slightly in the fridge – for about 20 minutes – before serving.

You could also make this recipe with ripe peaches. Blanch four peaches, skin and stone them, then liquidise the flesh with the finely grated zest and juice of 2 oranges, Greek yoghurt and sugar as above. Fold in the egg whites and freeze.

Menu Three

VEGETABLE MOULDS

These are very similar to the hot mousses made with fish or meat that we serve at Miller Howe, but which are made unctuous by lots of double cream. These are a much 'slimmer' alternative!

SERVES 4–6

12 oz (350 g) young carrots, trimmed
5 fl oz (150 ml) good chicken stock
1 oz (25 g) Parmesan cheese, grated
3 level tablespoons low-fat yoghurt
2 medium eggs
salt and freshly ground black pepper
2 tablespoons chopped fresh herbs
(parsley, mint, chervil or chives)

Pre-heat the oven to gas mark 4, 350°F (180°C).

Wash but do not peel the carrots, then slice them thickly. Place in a saucepan, cover with cold water and bring to the boil. Cook for 3 minutes, then strain. Pour on the chicken stock and then, over a low heat, continue cooking until the stock is absorbed (do not cover the pan).

Liquidise the carrots with all the remaining ingredients except for the herbs. (If they were added now you would end up with a dirty green mixture.) Fold the herbs into the mixture, then portion into four

157

large (3½ in/9 cm diameter) lightly oiled ramekins (or six smaller 3 in/7.5 cm ramekins). Place in a hot bain-marie and bake in the pre-heated oven for 30–40 minutes. Serve from the ramekins.

FISH AND VEGETABLES BAKED IN PAPER

White fish such as cod, halibut, sole or haddock contain only about 0.4–5 per cent fat, and therefore are extremely useful in any diet. Even oily fish such as salmon and mackerel contain only about 10–15 per cent fat (much less than meat). With prime cuts, the simplest cooking methods are often the best. Instead of the method below, you could bake or grill thin fillets of halibut, cod or salmon (halibut is nice baked with yoghurt and herbs); you could also steam prime pieces with flavourings such as stem ginger and lemon (good with halibut or cod), or lots of fresh herbs.

SERVES 4

1 lb (450 g) salmon, halibut, sole or cod, skinned and boned

2 oz (50 g) celery, finely chopped

2 oz (50 g) peeled onion, finely chopped

4 oz (100 g) each of carrot, fennel bulb, and button mushrooms, trimmed and finely chopped

fresh herbs (dill, fennel fronds, tarragon, parsley)

juice of 1 fresh lime

salt and freshly ground black pepper

Pre-heat the oven to gas mark 6, 400°F (200°C).

Make sure that any bones have been completely removed from the fish, then cut the flesh into strips.

Over a pan of boiling salted water, steam all the finely chopped vegetables (except for the mushrooms) for about 6–8 minutes.

Cut out four 8-in (20-cm) squares of good grease-proof paper and lay out on the work surface. Divide the steamed vegetables between the squares, with the fish strips on top. Add the mushrooms and herbs, and sprinkle with lime juice and lots of seasoning.

Fold the paper into a package, sealing each one well, then put on a baking tray in the pre-heated oven. Bake for 8 minutes. Allow your guests to open the packages at the table so that they can all relish the wonderful aromas.

The small soft bones of fish like whitebait and canned salmon, sardines or mackerel, should be eaten as they are full of calcium.

APPLE AND LIME GALETTES

Usually I serve these nutty galette biscuits in piles of three, sandwiched together with double cream and buttery sweet caramelised apples. The following filling is very much less fattening, and a simple dietary solution is to serve two biscuits instead of three to yourself (and any others in a similar condition)!

SERVES 4

Nutty galette pastry

3 oz (75 g) softened butter
2 tablespoons caster sugar
4 oz (120 g) plain flour
3 oz (75 g) ground hazelnuts

Apple and lime filling

juice of 2 limes
finely grated zest of 1 lime
8 oz (225 g) Bramley apples, peeled and cored weight
1 oz (25 g) caster sugar

To serve

4 heaped dessertspoons *fromage frais*

For the pastry, beat the butter and sugar together until very light, fluffy and creamy. Fold in the flour and ground hazelnuts. Place in a plastic bag and chill in the fridge for an hour or so. Remove from the fridge and allow to come back to room temperature before using.

Pre-heat the oven to gas mark 4, 350°F (180°C), and have ready a baking tray lined with good greaseproof paper.

Roll the pastry out on a floured surface to about ¼ in (5 mm) in thickness. Cut into twelve × 3 in (7.5 cm) circles. Transfer these circles to the prepared baking tray and bake in the pre-heated oven for 10 minutes. Cool well on a rack so that they remain crisp.

For the filling, put the lime zest and juice into a heavy-based pan. Slice in the apples, then cover and cook over a *very low* heat until the apples 'fall'. Shake the pan occasionally. Keep the lid on as the steam will cook the apples.

Add the caster sugar, stir in and dissolve thoroughly in the hot apple. Allow the apple to cool completely.

Spread some *fromage frais* on four of the biscuits, and top with some of the apple filling. Top each of these with another biscuit, then depending on who's on a diet or not, repeat the *fromage frais*, apple filling and biscuit topping so that you have either four three-layer puddings, or three, plus one with only two layers, and one biscuit left over! (Or any similar combination . . .)

Menu Four

PASTA WITH PESTO

There is a wealth of pasta types and shapes around. The pungent sauce can be stored in a screw-top jar in the fridge. It can be mixed with some crème fraîche *or yoghurt to make an unusual salad dressing, or made into the tasty salad addition on p. 84. You can also make the sauce using other herbs instead of the traditional basil — try parsley in particular.*

SERVES 4

**12 oz (350 g) pasta
(noodles, spirals, spaghetti, etc)
salt**

Pesto sauce

**2 garlic cloves, peeled
2 oz (50 g) fresh basil leaves
2 oz (50 g) pine kernels
4 tablespoons sunflower oil
2 oz (50 g) Parmesan cheese, finely grated
5 fl oz (150 ml) good white or rosé wine**

Cook the pasta in boiling salted water according to the instructions on the packet. Try to *under-* rather than over-cook it. Drain well, and keep hot.

Meanwhile, make the sauce. Put all the ingredients except for the cheese and wine into a food processor

162

or blender and whizz to mix well. Fold in the Parmesan then 'let down' gently with the wine.

Pour over the hot pasta, and serve in hot soup bowls, with perhaps a sprig of basil or parsley to decorate, and a *little* extra grated Parmesan if you must and can't resist.

LAMB'S LIVER WITH ORANGE

Offal is low in fat, and it is very good for you. Serve with some crunchy steamed vegetables.

SERVES 4

1 lb (450 g) lamb's liver, sliced thinly and sinews removed
juice and finely grated rind of 1 orange
salt and freshly ground black pepper
8 oz (225 g) onions, peeled and diced
1 tablespoon olive oil

Pre-heat the oven to gas mark 5, 375°F (190°C).

Marinate the slices of liver in the orange juice and zest with some freshly ground black pepper for a few hours prior to cooking (in the fridge in a covered bowl).

Fry the diced onion in the olive oil, until well and truly browned. Drain and remove from the pan.

Remove the liver from its marinade and seal in the remains of the onion cooking oil – make sure you use a very high heat to seal the meat speedily rather than letting it stew. Once sealed, immediately return the onions, pour on the marinade and add salt to taste. As soon as the marinade bubbles, transfer to a casserole dish, cover and bake in the pre-heated oven for 20 minutes.

POACHED NECTARINES WITH WARM SABAYON

Poached nectarines (or peaches) are delicious to have available in the fridge, both for the dieter and for guests. The poaching liquid here is very much less syrupy than usual, and the warm sabayon, if not exactly calorie-free, is slightly less sinful than double cream.

SERVES 4

4 just ripe nectarines (or peaches)
6 fl oz (175 ml) water
1–2 oz (25–50 g) caster sugar
4 cloves
4 allspice berries

Warm sabayon

3 egg yolks
3 oz (75 g) caster sugar
6 fl oz (175 ml) white wine

Blanch the nectarines by plunging them into boiling water for a few seconds, then into cold. Remove the skins, and halve the fruit, discarding the stones.

Place the measured water and sugar (the amount depends on the ripeness of the fruit) into a pan large enough to hold the nectarine halves. Heat to melt the sugar, then add the nectarine halves and the spices. Bring to the boil, then cover, reduce the heat and simmer gently for about 10 minutes or until the fruit is tender. Leave to cool in the syrup.

For the sabayon, cream the yolks and sugar in a bowl over a pan of simmering water. When pale, keep beating (a balloon whisk is ideal), and trickle in the white wine. Keep beating as the sauce becomes thick and frothy and heats through. Serve warm with the cold drained fruit.

Menu Five

COD IN YOGHURT WITH FENNEL BROTH

Although very simple, this dish is very satisfying — the broth is intensely flavoured and the cod is delicious after its yoghurt marination. It can all be prepared in advance and brought together at the last minute.

SERVES 4

11 oz (300 g) cod fillet, skinned and boned
salt and freshly ground black pepper
7 fl oz (200 ml) natural yoghurt
5 oz (150 g) tomatoes, skinned, de-seeded and diced
4 level teaspoons chopped fresh dill or parsley

Broth

2 bulbs of fennel, weighing about 1¼ lb (550 g), trimmed and coarsely chopped
4 oz (100 g) onions, peeled and diced
7 fl oz (200 ml) water
7 fl oz (200 ml) dry white wine
Pernod or some chopped fresh dill

Dice the prepared cod, then season. Marinate in the yoghurt in a tightly sealed container for 12 hours in the fridge.

To make the broth, put the fennel and onion in a large pan with the water and wine, and simmer for 1 hour. Strain and discard the vegetables, retaining the liquid. Taste this, and if the flavour is not intense enough, add some Pernod – up to a tablespoon – or some chopped dill.

When you wish to serve, pre-heat the oven to gas mark 4, 350°F (180°C).

Divide the marinated fish between four ovenproof bowls and warm through in the oven for 10 minutes. Reheat the broth to boiling point. Pour over the fish in the bowls and garnish with the prepared tomatoes and chopped herbs.

PEPPERY FILLET STEAK

*These steaks are very peppery in flavour, but wonderful
served hot or cold. A good salad is all that's needed to
accompany but if you were feeling 'binge-y', you could
have a small baked potato as well (no butter!).*

SERVES 4

4 × 4 oz (100 g) fillet steaks

1 tablespoon black peppercorns, roughly crushed

2 garlic cloves, peeled, and crushed to a paste
with 1 teaspoon runny salt

1 teaspoon Worcestershire sauce

Pre-heat the oven to gas mark 8, 450°F (230°C).

Make a paste with the peppercorns, garlic, salt and
Worcestershire sauce. Use this to paint both sides of
the steaks. Place on a baking tray and cook in the
pre-heated oven for 5 minutes each side for a pink
middle, or 7 minutes each side for less pink.

ORANGE AND SULTANA CHEESECAKE

An uncooked lemon cheesecake was one of my earliest successes – but since then I have evolved many ways of varying the recipe, using coffee, nuts, fruit, chocolate and alcohol. I've now gone a stage further, making a delicious basic recipe which is slightly less damaging for the figure! I've changed the base, included low-fat soft cheese and crème fraîche, and have considerably reduced the sugar content.
As before, the recipe will make a cheesecake to fill a 10 in (25 cm) loose-bottomed cake tin.

SERVES 8–10

Base
8 oz (225 g) Jordan's crunchy oats
2½ oz (65 g) butter, melted

Cheesecake
4 oz (100 g) sultanas
3 tablespoons Grand Marnier
2 tablespoons orange juice
½ oz (15 g) powdered gelatine
3 eggs, separated
8 oz (225 g) low-fat soft cheese
1 oz (25 g) caster sugar
10 fl oz (300 ml) *crème fraîche*
finely grated zest of 2 oranges

Soak the sultanas in the 5 tablespoons of liquid overnight.

Line the cake tin with greaseproof paper and pre-heat the oven to gas mark 2, 300°F (150°C).

For the base, mix the oats with the melted butter. Press into the paper-lined tin, smooth down, then bake for about 10 minutes only. Leave to cool.

For the cheesecake, strain the sultanas, keeping the liquid. Put the gelatine in a small pan, and add the liquid all in one go. Swirl the pan around until the gelatine dissolves. Put to one side.

Beat the egg yolks lightly, then beat into the soft cheese along with the sugar and *crème fraîche*. Add the orange zest and sultanas, then fold in the stiffly beaten egg whites.

Reconstitute the gelatine over a *very low* heat until the rather sticky mixture melts evenly. Strain the gelatine through a small warmed metal sieve into the mixture and fold in thoroughly.

Pour the mixture on to the cooled biscuit base and place in the fridge to set (about 6–8 hours).

Never keep any leftovers – throw them away, or give them to your equivalent of Ozzie!

Menu Six

BEETROOT AND ORANGE CUSTARDS

Serve these tasty little custard moulds out of the rame-kins as the starter for a dinner party, or, accompanied by a good crisp salad, as a delicious healthy lunch.

SERVES 4

2 cooked beetroots, approx. 4 oz (100 g) in weight

Custard

7 fl oz (200 ml) skimmed milk
2 tablespoons natural yoghurt
2 eggs, beaten
finely grated rind of 1 orange
1 level teaspoon ground cumin
¼ teaspoon soft brown sugar
salt and freshly ground black pepper

Pre-heat the oven to gas mark 4, 350°F (180°C).

Coarsely grate the beetroot on a double thickness of kitchen paper – this will help absorb excess moisture. (Use rubber gloves to keep your hands from staining!) Leave the beetroot to drain while you make the custard. Simply combine remaining ingredients in a bowl and blend thoroughly.

Divide beetroot between four 3½ in (9 cm) rame-kins, and pour over the custard. Bake in a hot bain-marie in the oven for 60 minutes. Cool slightly before eating.

ASPARAGUS CUSTARDS

SERVES 4

8 thin fresh asparagus spears
**1 oz (25 g) sunflower seeds, toasted in the pre-heating
oven for 15 minutes**

Custard

5 fl oz (150 ml) skimmed milk
3 rounded tablespoons *crème fraîche*
2 eggs, beaten
2 good pinches grated nutmeg
salt and freshly ground black pepper

Pre-heat the oven as before. Part-cook the asparagus by boiling or steaming for just 2 minutes, then drain, cool and dry. Cut into 1 in (2.5 cm) lengths.

Divide the asparagus between the four ramekins, then pour in the combined custard ingredients. Top with the toasted seeds, then bake as before.

Don't fight hunger pains – they are your body's way of telling you something important – but satisfy them with a *healthy* food.

LEEK AND ORANGE CUSTARDS

SERVES 4

4 oz (100 g) leeks, cleaned and diced
2 teaspoons olive oil
finely grated zest of 1 orange
1 oz (25 g) pine kernels, toasted (as opposite)

Custard

5 fl oz (150 ml) skimmed milk
3 rounded tablespoons Greek yoghurt
2 eggs, beaten
a few pinches of grated nutmeg
salt and freshly ground black pepper

Pre-heat the oven as before. Fry the leek dice in the olive oil until soft, then add the grated orange zest.

Divide the leeks between the four ramekins, then pour in the combined custard ingredients. Top with the toasted pine kernels, then bake as before.

CHICKEN BREASTS WITH GHERKIN AND MUSTARD CRUST

It sounds odd, perhaps, but tastes wonderful. The oil and the vinegar from the gherkins seem to seep into the chicken, making the flesh lovely and succulent.

SERVES 4

4 × 5–6 oz (150–175 g) chicken breasts, skin removed
salt and freshly ground black pepper
3 oz (75 g) pickled gherkins, drained
3 fl oz (85 ml) olive oil
3 teaspoons dry English mustard powder

Pre-heat the oven to gas mark 7, 425°F (220°C).

Arrange the chicken breasts on a small baking tray or dish, and season with salt and pepper.

Place the remaining ingredients in the food processor and give them a quick single whizz. The gherkins must be in fine pieces, not reduced to a purée. Divide this mixture over the tops of the chicken breasts to form a thick crust. Place in the pre-heated oven and cook for 20 minutes. Serve immediately.

Choose fish and poultry dishes more often than red meat.

FRUIT JELLY

Before I became evangelical about my weight and health, I used to make those jellies with sweet white wines or Frangelico, a nut liqueur; and a boozy port and claret jelly is one of the perennial favourites at Miller Howe. This is a fresher, 'thinner' alternative.

Using aspic or gelatine to make your own jellies is by far the best option. A packet of commercial jelly cubes contains no less than 19 teaspoons of sugar.

SERVES 4

about 12 oz (350 g) soft summer fruits
¾ oz (20 g) soft brown sugar (optional)
1 packet good-quality aspic powder (½ oz/15 g)
10 fl oz (300 ml) clear fruit juice

Prepare the fruits and divide them between four pretty glasses. Sprinkle with the sugar if using.

Prepare the aspic according to the instructions on the packet, using the juice instead of water (or wine), and leave to cool. Just before it begins to set, divide between the glasses. Leave to cool, cover with cling film and chill in the fridge.

Remove from the fridge about 20 minutes before serving so that the flavours can come alive.

CHAPTER 4

EATING
OUT

I think I lead an extremely charmed life, but most of my mates are horrified at what I actually get through each month – both work-wise and food-wise. I must admit that I am a bit of a workaholic: I thrive on a full diary; I adore looming deadlines; and I endeavour to put a quart into a pint pot each and every day. I inherit this, I think, from my much loved grand-mother. Her lot, though, was the dreariest sort of drudgery – shopping, cooking, cleaning and washing to make ends meet – but I seldom saw her without a smile on her face and an outstretched helping hand. As she said time and time again, 'What you sow, you reap . . . and you're a long time dead'!

Whenever I take a break from the hotel, I seem to spend it working. I'll fly to New York or South Africa to spread the word about British food; I'll demon-strate my style of cooking to audiences from Land's End to John O'Groats; I'll tour the New World to taste and buy wines for the hotel; and I'll try out restaur-ants here and abroad for my articles in *Lloyd's Log* and, until recently, the *Radio Times*. It all involves a lot of eating out. I'll also take some time to meet pals in old familiar places (one binge that I will *not* give up is blinis and caviar at The Russian Tea Room in New York), and go to friends' houses for lunch, tea or dinner.

The thought, therefore, of allying this way of life to a new puritanism was a little daunting at first to me. But it would have been unrealistic to expect to have every meal at home once embarked on my new healthy eating plan. Eating out with friends, after all, is one of life's joys, a happy sociable occasion, and you cannot become reclusive and *anti*-social just because you are dieting. You just have to be even more wary and rigorous, as meals out, whether in restaurants or in other people's houses, can be full of pitfalls.

However, if a celebration party or a particularly important business lunch is coming your way, and you feel you might like to fall off your pedestal a little, you can prepare to a certain extent by reducing your intake a little in the days beforehand. This will allay your conscience slightly. (It's also marginally easier than cutting down in the days *following* the occasion; there's nothing then to look forward to!)

In Restaurants

Even though I am surrounded by and work with food daily, the prospect of a meal out still thrills me. I always, but always, go into a restaurant with one

When you *can't* have a diet meal, eat moderately and replace the next meal with something light and sensible.

179

object in mind and one only – to have a damned good time. The atmosphere, the buzz and the smell of a good restaurant will always entrance me, and as I'm usually accompanied by people I love, I wouldn't give up that pleasure for the world.

In the fat old days, I used to order whatever took my fancy and to hell with the consequences. I enjoy myself just as much these days, but now carefully plan my intake and carefully read the menus. I also try and influence the *choice* of restaurant if I can, selecting one which I think will best suit my new healthier way of eating – which serves food cooked without heavy sauces or lots of fat.

Another tip is to cut down on the number of courses: preferably have a main course and fruit for dessert only, or a starter plus a main course *or* dessert. Three courses are wonderful, but you can get by quite happily on two. Drink mineral water – by far the most fashionable choice for business lunches these days – or, if you're following my scheme of things, get stuck in!

EUROPEAN RESTAURANTS

STARTERS These were always my downfall before, as anything in puff pastry with a cream sauce immediately caught my eye. A particular favourite used to be an extremely rich and boozy duck liver pâté piped on to a well-cooked, buttered croûton surrounded by

180

warm, heavily reduced Madeira cream sauce garnished with glazed pecan nuts . . . I used to groan in ecstasy as each mouthful was devoured. Nowadays, I think I would groan in agony as my system has become unused to such dishes.

What I look for now is any simple fish starter such as grilled mussels, a chilled fruit cocktail, melon, grapefruit, tomato and basil salad or, for that matter, any salad available that day. I will always ask that I dress a salad myself. Once upon a time I used to *drown* salads with a heavy walnut-oil-based dressing but now I find that I pour about a dessertspoon on the top and in the middle and then flick it around using my knife and fork. Provided my first few mouthfuls give me the flavour of a French dressing I mind not if, as the dish diminishes, I then get more or less only the taste of the salad itself.

A simple well-made consommé is something not to be sniffed at, and if served with a little dry sherry in it it sniffs pretty good. At least you can *see* that there's nothing too damaging in it! Home-made vegetable soups, provided they aren't showered with buttery rich croútons and dollops of lightly whipped cream do no harm to the figure and are quite filling. Simply avoid the bread, or take a small brown wholemeal roll and eat it without a trace of butter. However vulgar it may sound, you could dip it in your soup or consommé, or put the merest touch of French dressing on it as you would butter.

181

Other choices could be a little smoked salmon – not too fattening so long as you can avoid the accompanying brown bread and butter. If you like oysters, these would be fine for a dieter, as would grilled prawns or similar.

Most European restaurants would be able to offer one at least of the above. Avoid above all the pâtés, salamis, sausages and deep-fried delicacies of French, Italian and Spanish restaurants, and the starter dips of Greek restaurants. I love pasta, and it's often on Italian menus as a starter: I would ask whether I could have it as a main course, and start with a salad or finish with fruit.

MAIN COURSES I always seek out either a roast (only in a restaurant I know), or something grilled or barbecued in a new place. Should the grilled sole be accompanied by a cream herb sauce, this I will decline when ordering. Likewise a grilled steak with a béarnaise sauce. However, when I order a grilled steak (usually rump with the fat on), I ask for it to be cooked medium *but* immediately remove the fat when it is on my plate (and secrete it in a doggie bag for dear Ozzie!). A steak grilled without the fat is no pleasure for me. The fact that I can actually now remove the strip of luscious pure cholesterol, and not attempt to devour it, makes me feel grand.

Involve the waiter in any dilemmas. He should not take exception if you ask a few pertinent questions.

Guess what I've brought back for you Ozzie!
Steak fat. He's trying to kill me
Gray

Is the chicken breast cooked with the skin on or is it pan-fried in oil? Can the chicken be cooked in foil simply with a little white wine and fresh herbs? Is it possible for the veal escalope to be cooked plainly without breadcrumb coating and butter? Good waiters won't mind. In fact, if they have any sense, they will know you will appreciate their efforts and return again.

If, like me, you adore calves' liver and it is to be cooked with bacon, have it cooked with the bacon and allow the bacon flavour to enhance the liver. Just don't put any of the bacon in your gob. I have actually found that the merest hint of a favourite flavour settles my taste-buds. Pan-fried sweetbreads and kidneys are another offal treat I adore, but I simply request that they be sealed without any oil or fat and this is always done. In fact it saves the kitchen a bob or two!

ACCOMPANIMENTS If the vegetables come along with the main course as part of the meal, ask if it is possible for your potatoes to be boiled without butter and for at least one vegetable to be steamed. If there is to be a problem I often ask for a small portion of perfectly plain pasta to accompany my main course. This, with half a teaspoon of grated Parmesan and lots of freshly ground black pepper, happily suffices. I have occasionally asked for my vegetables not to be cooked, but served raw. With the merest touch of oil and vinegar (along with a little mustard), you will soon realise how delicious they are like this.

Good *haute cuisine*, French, Italian and Greek restaurants should be able to provide any or all of these.

DESSERTS If I have a dessert, most restaurants can offer a slice of melon or a bowl of fresh fruit salad. Avoid the dessert trolleys and cream at all costs!

EASTERN RESTAURANTS

Occasionally I eat Chinese or Japanese, but it's difficult to choose sensibly unless you're very familiar with culinary styles and menu names. A lot of Japanese food on offer is raw fish, which is fine; some Chinese soups and whole fish or seafood dishes are a good choice (many will have been steamed), but most meats and vegetables are cooked in lots of oil in the wok. Indian restaurants are less easy: the only sauce-less foods are dry-baked in the *tandoor* oven (*tandoori* or *tikka*). Thai cuisine, with its miraculous flavour combinations of coconut and lemongrass, is, I'm afraid, anathema on the whole to the serious weight-watcher. There may be only a few steamed fish dishes which would be suitable.

One benefit of most good eastern restaurants is that they should offer a selection of fresh fruit as a dessert – exotics such as mangoes, guavas, pineapple etc. It's much easier here as well to eschew alcohol, if that's your inclination, and stick to either water or green tea.

In Friends' Houses

At the beginning of my new way of life, when eating in friends' houses, I simply made no mention of my diet whatsoever (I adore their company too much). I went for whatever was on offer and then had to make up for it in the following few days. I used to literally starve myself throughout the whole day (a stupid thing to do as the pre-dinner glasses of wine went quite quickly to one's head!) then sit there, allowing myself to be cajoled into having second helpings. Folk think that because you are a food person you will be doing them the greatest compliment by eating twice as much as anybody else!

I put on a brave face for about four months and followed this pattern, but it was excruciating as my body had already adapted to less food. So I took myself in hand. Now, when accepting any invitation, I always say that I would *love* to come, but that I have a serious diet problem. I tell everyone that I cannot eat fats and rich sauces, and that I never ever take a second helping. In fact when the hosts see my trimmer figure, they realise what I have achieved and that I am not to be tempted. After all, diabetics and

You'll have another slice of Tiramisu won't you John..?. What a question!

those on gluten-free diets have to cope with a similar situation, and how I admire them. Most hosts and hostesses should be sympathetic, perhaps even a little envious of your will-power, and will rise to the challenge.

Don't let yourself be bullied over your new-found way of life but, at the same time, don't become a prissy prat looking as if you are the kitten having landed with its paws in the butter.

INDEX